Streams of Culture

OTHER BOOKS BY SIR GAVIN DE BEER

Growth
Vertebrate Zoology
The Elements of Experimental Embryology
(*with Julian Huxley*)
The Development of the Vertebrate Skull
On Shelley
(*with E. Blunden and S. Norman*)
Early Travellers in the Alps
Alps and Men
Archaeopteryx
Embryos and Ancestors
Sir Hans Sloane and the British Museum
The Sciences Were Never at War
Charles Darwin
Atlas of Evolution
The First Ascent of Mont Blanc
(*with T. Graham Brown*)
Voltaire's British Visitors
(*with A.-M. Rousseau*)
Reflections of a Darwinian
Gibbon and His World
Hannibal's March

STREAMS

of

CULTURE

❋

Sir Gavin de Beer

J. B. LIPPINCOTT COMPANY

Philadelphia / New York

Contents

Introduction

"Two-Culture Man" ran the cross-head over a flattering review of a book in which I had written some chapters on biology, others on biography and history of science, and others again on problems of ancient history and archaeology. I don't like that sort of description, and in this case it represented the opposite of the views that I hold. It showed that the journalist had let himself be etched by the facile slogan that has bitten like acid into popular opinion—that in Western civilization there are two cultures.

Few are more aware than I of the unfortunate results of the attempts made by older universities in the middle of the last century, when they started to take their duties seriously, to instruct and to examine their students. In Oxford, Sir Henry Acland wrote to the Regius Professor of Divinity a letter in which he urged the duty of "providing against our graduates leaving the university in utter ignorance of the first principles of the great laws which are imposed on the material world." He went on to say that "the real value of the foundations of which I speak arises wholly from the services they perform for general liberal education, and not for detailed professional instruction." It is easy to see in these words the horror with which the guardians of pure education viewed anything approaching vocational training.

To rub in Acland's home truths, Robert Walker stressed how discreditable it was that anybody should pretend to be educated if he supposed that earth, air, fire, and water are the four elements of which the world is composed, and that the communications of the electric telegraph are made by "pulling the wires." There is a contemporary story of a don who thought that the mercury barometer would look better on the wall of the common room of his college if it were placed horizontally instead of vertically. All this was barely more than a century ago.

The criticism slowly sank in, but in the wrong way. Honour Schools in Natural Science were instituted, to balance the Honour Schools in Humane Letters which had already been introduced. The first fundamental error committed was to make these curricula alternative and mutually exclusive, with the result that some graduates still leave the university without any idea of how their kidneys work, let alone a radio. At the same time, other graduates go down in comparative ignorance of the principles and values for which the humanities stand. This state of affairs has been parodied in the definition of a university as a place where students in the Arts faculties know no science and don't want to, while students in the Science faculties know little of the humanities but would like to know more.

The second great mistake was to go on the principle that as more and more is discovered, more and more must be taught. This inevitably leads to a premium on precociousness, for as economic reasons limit the time during which a student can be kept at university, time is borrowed, or rather mortgaged, at the other, earlier end of the curriculum, and specialization is pressed back into the schools. Advanced subjects are introduced prematurely at the expense of more general subjects, and worse still, the competitive nature of examinations for scholarships confers an advantage on the precocious, which is the exact opposite of one of the most important processes responsible for the evolution of man: delayed development, for reasons given in Chapter 4. Besides this, subjects introduced prematurely are only imperfectly appreciated, and at the expense of more basic subjects which are increasingly difficult to acquire at later ages. Mathematics and modern languages do not come so easily to students after they have spent so much precious young time with test-tubes and dissecting-dishes.

The situation got worse and worse as universities were misguided enough to allow their preliminary examinations to be taken direct from school, before coming up to university, so that all the time spent at university could be devoted to specialization. There are two remedies for this state of affairs: the first is to delay as long as possible the time when the decision to specialize in one subject has to be taken at university; the second is to discourage specialization at school, a difficult task in view of the prestige which a school acquires from the number of scholarships at university that it wins, like a goose-farm, by producing fatter geese in shorter time.

I tackled the first of these cures by getting the university of Oxford to adopt a new set of courses and examinations, Honour Moderations in Natural Science, in which students could for one year take any three of seven possible subjects before deciding to specialize in any one of them and then take their degree. The War prevented me from making progress with the second method of cure, but Sir Henry Tizard tried it with marked success at the Imperial College of Science and Technology in London. It consisted in offering scholarships for study in science on examinations in which there were no compulsory science questions at all. Only mathematics and English were compulsory. The percentage of students elected to scholarships under this scheme who subsequently obtained First Classes was no lower than that of students who had been awarded scholarships after examination in the science which they had been taught at school.

This ability to cross over from the arts faculties to science with success was not unexpected, and in itself it serves to break down the barrier between the two sets of subjects. The best men of science whom I have known began with a classical education, and it may be remarked that two of the greatest British scientists of this century, Sir D'Arcy Thompson and Sir Cyril Hinshelwood, one a biologist and the other a chemist, were Presidents of the Classical Association. Paul Valéry is another example of a man for whom there were no watertight compartments in knowledge.

With the progress in science during the last half-century, the situation has really become easier to cope with, without anyone's noticing it, not in spite of that progress but because of it. Sir Peter Medawar has reminded us that whereas in the early decades of this century the different branches of science were in chaos, the discoveries that have since been made throw light on general principles of increasing breadth which require for their teaching a few well-selected examples, leaving the whole unwieldy mass of detail growing like a snowball, to be acquired later and to fall into place, if necessary. In biology, at any rate, it is all so much more tidy that there is no justification for the precocity-scramble.

The situation has also become easier because of the increasing realization of a great truth of which sight should never have been lost: the mental processes involved in observation, verification, and use of the imagination in producing ideas are fundamentally the same in poets, essayists, artists, musicians, and scientists. This is why the notion of

"Two Cultures" is exaggerated, because the idea widens the gap that exists and makes it more difficult to fill, when it is only a temporary dichotomy of educational policy and practice between the arts and the sciences.

A "culture" is a body of knowledge and an accepted method of thought available to individuals in a civilization, capable of improvement or refinement by education and training. In the Western world, thanks to a few geniuses such as Francis Bacon, Galileo Galilei, René Descartes, Isaac Newton, and Charles Darwin, there is a generally accepted system of thinking, of searching for truth, and of ideals of moral and material betterment for mankind which constitutes a single culture.

This becomes apparent when Western culture is compared with a really different culture, such as that of India, which is difficult for Westerners to grasp. Stepping stones towards it include propositions such as the following: only partial truths are unambiguous; paradox is the only reliable insurance against missing some of the essential components of truth; contradictions are the very stuff out of which higher truth is wrought; once truth is thought to have been achieved, communication ceases; every being, so far as it is a being, is made out of nothing. These existentialist utterings of Martin Heidegger, Karl Jaspers, and Jean-Paul Sartre may help, but perhaps more is needed before it is possible for a Westerner to understand the Upanishads or Jainism fully, or the thoughts of Mao Tse-tung on antagonistic and non-antagonistic contradictions. Here, it would surely be legitimate to speak of two cultures.

However, Western culture is so rich that it is split into a number of streams. If each of these streams were to be dignified with the name of "culture," there would be far more than two of them. In the branches of science itself, there would be several. There would be one for the mathematicians, who really practise a "creative art," as one of their leading representatives assured me. This is intelligible to many in the stream of physicists and chemists, but unintelligible to all but rare exceptions in the stream of biologists. Engineers and technologists form another stream, and so, of course, do those who follow the various liberal arts. Yet they all make use of the same mental processes, and in particular of the gift of imagination, the creative "art." The scientist in coming to a decision on how to interpret his results has to make use of criteria which, in themselves, are not scientific but standards of value appertaining to truth. Poets, artists, and musicians constantly make use of a technique sometimes regarded as exclusively "scientific": they experiment, with verse-form or metre, composition and colour, theme-development or form. As in the case of scientists, if any progress is to be made, the first thing to do is to have an idea, and then to test it and see how it works.

A recent writer, Anthony Jackson, referring to Newton's Laws of Motion, said, "It is the theories that explain the laws which really matter, and it is these that are scientific ideas." What is a "scientific idea"? When Malthus developed the idea (it was not his) that the rate of increase of the population in man was inevitably bound to out-strip the rate of production of his food supply, the argument was un-sound because, even today, nobody knows or has tried to discover how much human food supply could be increased if its production benefited from the highest priority and the most efficient techniques. If it was a "scientific idea," it was false. Did it become "scientific" when Darwin took the idea, turned it upside down, and applied it not to man and his increasable food supply, but to animals which have no means of im-proving their food supply, and saw that it provided the sanctions which enforce the action of natural selection in improving adaptation to the environment and bringing about evolution? What makes this example particularly instructive is that Malthus had no idea of natural selection at all; that idea was Darwin's, and it is difficult to see what advantage is gained by applying to an idea the qualification of "scientific." Some ideas, like those of Shelley, as Desmond King-Hele has shown, would have to be labelled "poetical" as well as "scientific." Ideas are ideas, the most wonderful and the most dangerous things in the world.

Nobody can read the epic story of how James Watson and Francis Crick solved the problem of the structure of deoxyribonucleic acid, DNA, the stuff of which hereditary genes are composed, and showed how it threw light on such fundamental processes as replication, the genetic code, synthesis of living matter, and embryonic development, without failing to be struck by the analogy with a poet's search for the means of expressing the truths which he wishes to convey, or an artist or a composer wrestling with his means of expression. With the data which Watson and Crick had to go on, partly stereochemical involving the spatial relations of atoms to one another in a molecule, partly quantum-mechanics governing the energy-relations in the parts of a molecule, and partly the patterns revealed by M. H. F. Wilkins's analysis of the distribution of atoms in the molecule, what they needed was an idea of how certain constituents *might* be arranged. They had many ideas which they had to discard as they failed to fit one or other of the (few) given facts; but eventually they hit on the right one.

So scientists make discoveries as a result of having ideas, and the history of science is full of them. I have referred to some in the first three chapters of this book. The picture of a scientist as spending all his time grubbing in his laboratory, with his nose in a test-tube or a dissecting-dish, is very imperfect and incomplete. What, then, is a scientist, and what is natural science?

Sydney Ross has reminded us that the word "scientist" was coined by William Whewell in 1834, on the model of artist, economist, atheist, "to describe a cultivator of science in general." That he felt the need for such a word shows that he wanted to curb the "increasing proclivity of separation and dismemberment" which was already in evidence.

There remains the question of what science is. The stock answer is to refer to the motto of the Royal Society: *nullius in verba,* meaning that conclusions are based not on what any man says or thinks or prefers, but on what observation and experiment show. This is of course very important, and it is by letting nature make her own pronouncements that her laws have been discovered, not to be reversed even by George III when he remonstrated with the President of the Royal Society because of the preference given to the lightning conductor devised by Benjamin Franklin, then a rebel against his sovereign. It is, however, becoming doubtful whether, by itself, this definition is sufficient to denote natural science, because emphasis on objectivity and suppression of subjective preference can also be applied to subjects outside natural science, such as numismatics. There is also the fact that however objective a scientist may set out to be in his observations and experiments, these have already been formulated in terms of an hypothesis which he has chosen to adopt. At any rate, history cannot be a science, for its very subject-matter—aims, aspirations, and aversions of men—are exactly what science must eschew. Nor is science something of which "a decent amount can be ingested" in a given time, as a writer is reported to have said, as if it were a quantity of gas pumped into the tank of an automobile.

The reader of this book will find some very cogent thoughts devoted to the question of what science is, in essay-reviews of books by George G. Simpson and others, in Chapters 7, 8, and 9. Here, I must content myself with justifying the statement that there is no such thing as *the* scientific method. Observation, experiment (which means only that the observer puts himself into a privileged position from which to observe) and verification can be applied to many things, from archaeology to stamp-collecting, which are not natural science, as well as to physics, chemistry, and biology. The latter, scientific fields, differ from the former, "arts subjects," not in method of study, but in the object on which the study is made. If that object is a product of nature and not of man, such study may lead to the discovery of general principles, so-called laws of nature, such as gravitation, motion, evolution, natural selection, thermodynamics, indeterminacy, of universal application in nature. It is in the application of these general principles that man is able to exert an effect on nature (which does not always "know best"), whether by breeding of higher-yielding cultivated plants and domestic animals, treatment of infections by antibiotics or of accidents and pathological states by surgery, or discovery and use of sources of natural energy which in the history of civilization have been gravity, wind, steam, chemicals, electricity, internal combustion, and atomic.

Observation and experiment on manuscripts, coins, pictures, or anything else made by man produce results of great interest, such as the Vinland Map described in Chapter 12; but no general principles of universal application can result from such studies. Science, then, is the body of knowledge built up from the study of nature by observation and experiment, suggested by ideas.

It is sometimes boasted that man has reached such a state of proficiency in applied science that he can control his environment. He can already clear airfields of fog and produce rain if enough, and cold enough, carbon dioxide is dropped from airplanes. He could do many more things, but as he has shown himself lamentably incapable of controlling himself to his own best advantage, it is not true to say that he can control his environment to his own benefit. It certainly was true at the time he learnt to cultivate plants and to domesticate animals, as a result of which he passed from the precarious existence of the hunter-gatherer, without any reserves and always dependent on the luck of the chase, to that of the food-producer by agriculture, with enough at least for the morrow. That was the Neolithic Revolution, one of the few in the history of man which have done nothing but good.

By continuing on the same lines, man is still able to help himself. Louis de Vilmorin greatly increased the sugar-content in beetroot. By extracting the recessive type after crossing poor-yielding but rust-resisting wheat with a prolific strain, Sir Rowland Biffin produced a resistant form with a high yield, one of the classic examples of the application of genetics to agriculture. The good work continues. G. D. H. Bell has improved British barley to such an extent that whereas in 1963 the United Kingdom produced 4 million tons of barley and imported 1 million tons, in 1967 it produced over 8 million tons and exported 1 million, of the Proctor variety. Crossing and selecting have been applied not only to vines, but also to the yeasts which ferment grapes, with the result that more and stronger wine is produced.

Among animals, Louis Daubenton and Sir Joseph Banks greatly improved the quality and quantity of sheep wool after smuggling Merino sheep out of Spain and crossing them with their own varieties. The use of artificial insemination will help to improve breeds of cattle, and if the technique invented by B. C. Bhattacharya to predetermine the sex of these animals, by gravity-fractionation of male-producing and female-producing sperm, can be used successfully, the solution of the problem of hunger in India will be greatly advanced, because milk is the only food which Hindus allow cattle to supply to them. Race horses run faster. Man runs faster; and since Roger Bannister ran his mile under four minutes, and Jean-Claude Killy broke the ski speed record, we may see selective breeding in man to produce Olympic champions.

There are not wanting, however, examples of impending disaster from what is glibly called man's progress in the application of science. I do not refer to the ill-considered use of pesticides on crops, which kill earthworms, that invaluable (and unpaid) army of farm-labourers that prepare and aerate the soil, and which also kill wild birds with probably serious results to the balance of nature. I refer to applications to industry.

John Tyndall discovered about a hundred years ago that the carbon dioxide in the atmosphere exerts a "greenhouse effect" on the world because it allows the sun's rays to pass through it and to strike the earth; but the earth reflects much of this energy in the form of infra-red rays to which the carbon dioxide in the atmosphere is impervious. The result of bottling up this energy is to raise the temperature of the atmosphere. During the past hundred years, it is estimated that 400,000 million tons of carbon dioxide have been poured into the atmosphere from the combustion of coal and oil in industry, and every year some 11,000 million tons are now added. The average winter temperature in northern Europe has risen by 5 degrees Fahrenheit; in 1900 ships could reach Spitzbergen during three months of the year, now seven months. Pack-ice now seldom reaches Iceland; cod-fisheries and the belt of cyclones have moved northwards.

Geologists and physicists are watching the situation with some anxiety, for if the world temperature were to rise greatly, the ice-cap of Antarctica could melt, and that would raise the level of the oceans by about 100 feet. London and New York would be drowned; the President of France could draw comfort from the probability that the Place de la Concorde would be only just awash. If world temperatures do rise, the human race best adapted to heat is the Negro.

But events might take a very different turn. One of the probable contingent causes of the last Ice Age, put forward by Captain Robert Falcon Scott, who knew a great deal about ice, is the thawing of the Arctic Ocean, from whose open waters the winds could absorb moisture and deposit it on the ice-cap of Greenland, which, like a snowball, would soon spread not only in area but as a cold-generating zone, and so refrigerate the north temperate zone. If this is so, and if the Arctic Ocean is heated again, as it already appears likely to be, mankind will have to look forward to a return of the Ice Age. Indeed, temperature curves already established for the ten thousand years since the end of the last Ice Age show a maximum about 3000 B.C., since when there has been oscillation but a marked descent of the temperature curve, fairly symmetrical with its rise. In other words, we may now be not in a post-glacial phase, but in an interglacial phase, of which there were so many in the Ice Age, with even less pleasant prospects for London, New York, and Moscow, some few thousand years hence. The human race best adapted to withstand extreme cold is the Mongolian.

So much for man's control of his natural environment. What of his control of human nature, and the population explosion? This is where it becomes so obvious that the streams of culture in Western civilization are in such need of being reknit together, and of being guided not so much by politicians, philosophers, theologians, scientists or technologists as such, but by wise men and women. "But where shall wisdom be found? and where is the place of understanding?" This leads to mention of two streams of Western culture not so far brought into this discussion.

Philosophy is the first. Philosophers practise observation but not experiment. They trust and rely on the perfection of their instrument, the trained mind, to reach valid conclusions; but these are almost as numerous as philosophers, and the value of their work cannot be quickly tested, as in natural science. The term "natural philosopher" was the seventeenth-century way of expressing the meaning of natural scientist.

The last stream makes no use of either observation or experiment. It is theology, by which is not meant religion, but the systems of dogmatic beliefs that have been imposed on mankind. The extent to which the theologian, relying solely on what he believes to be the ultimate truth in so-called revealed texts and in tradition, is divorced from all the other streams of Western culture may be illustrated by the writings of Father J. O'Neill, who begins by asserting, "Since God is the author both of reason and revelation, there can be no discrepancy between the proved conclusions of science and the teachings of the Bible." He continues, "In view of the great obscurity in which the anthropologist labors, he ought to be grateful for the light shed on his subject by revelation." Seldom can there have been a more clear-cut confrontation between such radically different methods for the pursuit of truth. The writer then proceeds to give hostages to fortune when he says, "Whether the human race originated from one or more couples is a question to which anthropology will never be able to provide a definite answer. The answer has been provided by the Magisterium not because it is the function of the Magisterium to teach science, but because it is its duty to decide on those matters that pertain to the foundation of the Christian Religion." If in the last sentence he had said "Pauline" instead of "Christian" it would have accorded better with my interpretation of history. But he seems never to have heard of genetics, or population-genetics, and the light which they throw on anthropology. Darwin realized that in matters on which science is competent to speak, the Bible is no more to be trusted than the sacred books of the Hindus or the Mohammedans, to whom might now be added the Marxists. If he were alive today, Darwin would have concurred in the conclusion that species do not originate from single couples but from whole populations, sufficiently numerous to avoid the disastrous effects of incest (because it reduces variability), and to ensure a possibility of mutations and recombinations of genes providing enough variation on which natural selection can act, and act quickly enough to turn an australopithecine into a Venus of Milo and a Darwin in one million years. The estimated number of the original human population, when it emerged from the Primates one million years ago, is 125,000.

It would be easy, but perhaps unfair, to go on like this. If the Virgin Birth were true, Christ would have been haploid and had only half the normal number of chromosomes (unless the Holy Spirit is deoxyribonucleic acid, which I do not suppose Father O'Neill would admit), and half-size, as has been shown in all experiments on artificial parthenogenesis in vertebrates where haploid individuals have been produced. Women have one more X-chromosome than men, and therefore Eve could not have been formed out of the tissues of Adam (unless he was sex-reversed, and in that case they would have had no sons). As for more recent assertions, it would be interesting to compare the energy-thrust required to lift the Virgin Mary's house from Nazareth to Dalmatia, and from there to Loretto, in A.D. 1291, with that necessary to launch and propel an intercontinental ballistic missile or a space ship. It is for reasons such as these that theology is more isolated from other streams of Western culture than any other, and it is probably this which has led to the atrophy of churches in communities other than those which believe in mysticism and unverifiable faith, which some call superstition. The scientist has faith, in the orderliness of the universe. If there is a deep cleavage between streams of Western culture, it is between theology and the rest.

The divorce between the Roman theological stream and all rational streams has now been made complete by the encyclical *Humanae vitae*. In spite and in the teeth of all the evidence, which is now overwhelming, a body which claims Magisterium over the thoughts and lives of men has made a pronouncement affecting the physiology, psychology, ecology and genetics of man, ignoring a scientific informed opinion on all these subjects, and disregarding the warnings which are plain enough of the danger of the population bomb unless adequate precautions are taken, and in time, against the ghastly consequences of misery for all.

Protestant theologians start with the advantage of not having blotted their copy-books with such commands as require belief in transubstantiation, immaculate conception, bodily assumption of Mary, infallibility, and the Syllabus of Errors. They nevertheless have a sufficient burden of old assertions which are difficult to square with scientific knowledge. It was doubtless with this in view that the Archbishop of Canterbury some years ago contributed an essay of great interest to a Sunday newspaper, in which he raised the question of whether there had been an actual Fall of Man, or whether the interpretation might be that man had not risen as high or as fast from what he called "the mammalian species" as could have been hoped.

The Rev. Dr. E. L. Mascall, of Christ Church, Oxford, a leading theologian of the Church of England, is impressed by two conclusions, said by him to have been "reached on the biological side which are of the greatest theological interest." One is that man is unique, which so far is true; but when he attempts to derive theological significance from the statement that "all other branches of the evolutionary tree come to dead ends; the organisms are either too specialized to survive changes of environment, or too settled and sheltered to develop any further," the biologist is entitled to speak. He points out, first, that the principle by which all the major groups of successful animals (including man) have evolved is by discarding the old ancestral adult form and evolving from the young, the principle called paedomorphosis, which provides precisely the mechanism whereby specialization is overcome.

The biologist's second point is a direct answer to Dr. Mascall's second conclusion, that evolution by natural selection of heritable variations has come to an end. This might have been said at any time during the past 2,000 million years, had there then been anyone sufficiently rash to say it, and no biologist would say it now. It would take a long time, but if the human species disappeared, another species would eventually evolve into a dominating position, and it is impossible to forecast what its characters would be. With this idea in mind, Darwin wrote, "Any animal whatever, endowed with well-marked social instincts [which higher animals are], the parental and filial affections being here included, would inevitably acquire a moral sense or conscience, as soon as its intellectual powers became as well, or nearly as well developed, as in man."

The cleavage emerges from the Reverend Doctor's claim (or con-

fession) that the theologian believes that man has an unique supernatural destiny. There it is again, the old anthropocentric view of the
universe. Nature is quite wonderful enough for William of Occam's
razor to be applied to any attempt to account for matters difficult to
understand by appealing to the supernatural, before the bounds of the
natural are explored and found wanting. The supernatural may exist,
but no theologian has any right to think that biology supplies him with
evidence for it.

Most interesting in its desire to rescue religion from theology is the
recent study of the gospels by the Swiss pastor Charles Rittmeyer, to
which he felt driven by the shallowness, tendentiousness, and poverty
of exegesis as adduced up to the present. He has tried to do justice
to the real thoughts and principles of Jesus, which he sees to be rational
and modern, which means timeless, when freed from the Judaic,
Apostolic, and Pauline contexts which have hitherto hidden and deformed them. It is an attempt to prevent the baby Jesus from being
thrown out of the window with the bathwater of theology, now unacceptable to more and more, who realize that alleged revelations by personal gods and prophets, long-term specific prophecies based on erroneous
translations, and interference with the laws of nature weaken the
theologians' own arguments to the point where they become verbal
trickery, with which men who preserve intellectual integrity can have
nothing to do. It is fascinating, but at the same time saddening, to
notice how the interpretation of the revelation of Marx leads to disputes
and martyrdoms on account of so-called deviations, which can be put
in parallel with comparable disputes and persecutions for heresy, which
blacken the stream of theology.

Situations like those just described are straightforward. Shelley knew
very well and showed elegantly that when it comes to the adoption
of a belief, exercise of the will plays little part in it, and people take
their choice according to their upbringing, environment, and temperament. Children brought up by Jesuits sometimes become communists.
But it is much more regrettable when, under the cover of pseudo-
science, verbiage, and obscurity, propositions are put forward which
masquerade as science. Here it is impossible to pass over the writings
of that very charming but unfortunate man, Pierre Teilhard de Chardin.

There are people who actually believe that he had a claim to be
considered as a scientist because he accepted evolution (with the

restrictions that his theology imposed), and he described some fossils and geological beds, on the strength of which, utterly ignoring genetics, molecular biology, ecology, and experiments on natural selection, but accepting a form of psychological inheritance of acquired characteristics, he constructed a fairy tale on evolution which some wishful thinkers have hailed as a synthesis between science and religion. Example: "The more I have thought of the problem [of evolution], the more I have convinced myself that we are confronted by an effect, not of external forces, but of psychology. According to current opinion, a carnivorous animal would develop carnivorous instincts because its teeth became flesh-tearing and its claws became talons. Should not this proposition be exactly reversed? In other words, if the tiger has enlarged its teeth and sharpened its claws, is it not precisely because in its ancestry it received and developed a 'carnivorous soul'? And similarly with timid cursorial animals, swimmers, fossorial and flying animals. Evolution of characters, yes; but on condition that the term is taken to mean temperament" (*Le Phénomène Humain*, pp. 163–164). It is curious to see a Jesuit attributing souls to animals.

This moonshine was blown out of the water in his own country by Jean Rostand when he observed that "of a biologist, Teilhard has neither the training, nor the knowledge, nor the frame of mind." In Britain, Sir Peter Medawar rang down the curtain on Teilhard's pseudo-science, and on the fallacy of thinking that he had anything worth listening to on evolution, with the words, "a dotty euphoristic kind of nonsense. There is no real harm in it."

Teilhard dabbled in evolution, and this provides me with the opportunity to stake out a modest claim for what I have done in this field, to which I have devoted fifty years of scientific study. Some of the results are given in Chapters 4, 5, and 6 of this book. As a former Director of the British Museum (Natural History), and President of the XVth International Congress of Zoology which met in London in 1958 to celebrate the centenary of the first publication by Darwin and Alfred Russel Wallace on evolution by natural selection, I felt that it was up to me to systematize knowledge on this subject. This I have done in Chapter 4, and in my books *Charles Darwin* and *Atlas of Evolution*. My other claims are to have killed the theory of recapitulation and to have established in its place the notion of paedomorphosis and the modes of clandestine evolution (Chapter 5), and of mosaic evolution (Chapter 6), as principles which the transformation of animals during their descent have followed.

I hope that I have said enough to make a plea for regarding Western culture as a unit, so rich that it is divided into several streams which should be, and can be, knit together. In this I claim no priority whatever. For support it is not necessary to go back to René Descartes, or to go beyond the Huxley family. Thomas Henry Huxley: "Science and literature are not two things, but two sides of the same thing." Aldous Huxley: "The great truth that art and literature and science are one." Sir Julian Huxley: "No sensible man of science imagines for a moment that the scientific point of view is the only one. Art and literature, religion and humane studies, are other ways of exploring and describing the world." It may be added that these great agnostics were and are extremely religious men, but without revelation.

In addition to the basic threads which unite the various streams of Western culture, there is a special way in which they can be knitted together, which is to use techniques of natural science to solve problems in history and archaeology. Elsewhere, in my *Reflections of a Darwinian,* I have done this for the origin of the Etruscans, the identification of St. Michael's Mount in Cornwall with the classical Iktin described by Diodorus of Sicily, and the tracing of Hannibal's route over the Alps. Here, I have included three more such studies. One (Chapter 10) shows how genetics can throw light on the transition from the Neolithic to the Bronze Age in western Europe; another (Chapter 11) uses seismology and vulcanology, as well as other branches of geodesy, to show how Spyridon Marinatos and Angelos Galanopoulos have solved the problem of Atlantis; the last (Chapter 12) indicates how meteorology, oceanography, and botany confirm the traditions of the Norse discoverers of America. And "that," as a brother-officer said after a gruelling day in the last war, "is all I can do for the money."

Gavin de Beer

Streams of Culture

CHAPTER
1

Other Men's Shoulders

Text of a lecture delivered in the Arts/Science Lecture Programme of the University of Sussex on 12 May 1965. From
Annals of Science, volume 20, 1964 (1965).

With that sense of modesty allied to perfect taste which distinguishes
the really great, Isaac Newton said, "If I have seen further it is by
standing on ye sholders of Giants."[1]* Their names are such that any
man would have been proud to sail in their company; Copernicus,
Kepler, and Galileo come immediately to mind, and the importance
of their own contributions to knowledge serves to increase the eminence
of their great successor.

It is, of course, not sufficient to have had distinguished precursors;
the successor must have a flash of genius of his own, one of those
dangerous things called ideas, such as could be generated by the fall
of an apple. There are many examples in science of ideas sparked off
by accidents. It is a pity that the scepticism with which everything

* Superior figures refer to the Notes, pages 224–232.

should be tested has been abusively applied to the story of Newton's apple, for in his *Life of Newton* Sir David Brewster poured water on it so chilly that the story has been relegated to the realm of legend. Yet there is no reason to doubt the authenticity of William Stukeley's account of his visit to Newton at Orbels Buildings in Kensington on 15 April 1726, when Newton "was just in the same situation, as when formerly, the notion of gravitation came into his mind. It was occasion'd by the fall of an apple, as he sat in a contemplative mood. Why should that apple always descend perpendicularly to the ground, thought he to himself. Why should it not go sideways or upwards, but constantly to the earth's centre?"[2] The story is confirmed from sources in Newton's intimate circle in the very year of his death, 1727, by Robert Greene and by a man whose literary fame has eclipsed the contributions which he made to science, Voltaire,[3] who played a part insufficiently recognized in leading the men of science in continental Europe to adopt Newton's theories in preference to those of Descartes.

The shoulders on which Newton stood, and the still more numerous feet that stood on his shoulders, are common knowledge in physics and lead up to the present day with its elementary particles and anti-particles, matter and anti-matter. From Newton the chain also leads to modern chemistry, for it was from him that John Dalton derived the idea of atoms, particles of matter, that led from him through D. I. Mendeléeff to H. G. J. Moseley and atomic numbers.

The history of science, often misled by the misuse of hindsight, sometimes also suffers from gross errors perpetrated in its name which take the form of placing the praise on the wrong shoulders, perhaps for nationalist reasons. Once such an error has started, there seems to be no stopping it. A case of this is the legend that Friedrich Wöhler announced the synthesis of urea in his publication of 1828, and that he thereby broke down the distinction between inorganic and organic processes in Nature by producing in his test-tubes a substance known only as a product of animal life, urea.[4] Wöhler certainly obtained it, "without the help of a kidney or a living creature, man or dog," as he said; but it was no synthesis. Instead of compounding urea from the elements that compose it, he started with dried blood, hoofs, and horns and obtained urea as a product of breakdown of organic matter; yet even now the legend that Wöhler performed the first synthesis of an organic compound, and that he thereby drove vitalism out of organic chemistry, is still current. It perpetuates a grave injustice to Marcelin Berthelot who, in 1860, published his patient and painstaking synthesis of a series of organic compounds from their chemical elements.

A measure of the march which the physical sciences had stolen over the biological sciences may be gauged from the chaos that still reigned in the latter until the middle of the nineteenth century, while the former were drawn into order and endowed with general principles of universal validity in the seventeenth century. It is true that in the eighteenth century Linnaeus had codified a system of nomenclature and drawn up a scheme of classification which performed an invaluable service at a time when the numbers of known species of plants and animals, revealed by exploration, were increasing at such a rate that without Linnaeus's system the confusion in biology would have become irremediable. But no general principle was revealed thereby; the tables of the Vegetable and Animal Kingdoms presented a problem, that of their diversity, which they did not solve.

It must also be said that classification, studied by itself in the absence of soundly based unifying general principles, could lead to the most appalling nonsense. As late as 1821, William Sharp MacLeay[5] built up his quinarian theory, a mystical system of classification on the supposition that at all levels the Animal Kingdom is based on five groups arranged in a circle, each with affinities to its neighbours on both sides, each containing five subgroups arranged in a similar manner and so on, so as, in MacLeay's words, to "compose the whole province of zoology." Presently, Edward Newman[6] improved on this system by substituting the number 7 for 5, because God rested on the seventh day, Noah took 7 clean animals into the Ark, there were 7 plagues, 7 years of famine, 7 years of plenty, 7 golden candlesticks, 7 churches, 7 angels, and 7 spirits of God. It is not usually realized, without any wish to be irreverent, how deep the morass of biology still was at a date comparatively so recent, which serves to emphasize the paucity of biological shoulders available to stand on before Darwin and Mendel.

The debt that science owes to Darwin is twofold.[7] First, he collected and presented the evidence on which it is impossible to doubt that organic evolution of plants and animals has occurred, and, second, he put forward the theory of natural selection to explain how it has occurred. These two contributions to science present some pretty problems in the tracing of ideas to their sources and of the creative processes in the mind.

In the demonstration of the fact of evolution, Darwin expressly disclaimed any priority for himself. Early in September, 1838, he wrote:[8] "Seeing what von Buch, Humboldt, G. St Hilaire, and Lamarck have written I pretend to no originality of ideas—(although I arrived at them quite independently and have used them since) the line of proof and reducing facts to law only merit if merit there be in following work." Darwin's independent arrival at these ideas refers, of course, to his own observations and meditations during the voyage of the *Beagle* on the distribution of different species in adjacent regions and the boundaries between them, the similarities between fossil and living forms in the same areas, the South American character of the birds of the Galapagos Islands, and the diversity in those islands of the ecological niches and of the various adaptations of the birds to them.[9] Here Darwin stood on nobody's shoulders but his own feet.

The list of names given in the note just quoted is interesting not only for those that it includes but for those that it omits. Leopold von Buch and Alexander von Humboldt are there not because they believed in evolution, but because they suggested that species were the products of local varieties of other species, protected from interbreeding with the main form of those species by geographical isolation, a suggestion which Darwin adopted.[10] The names of Lamarck and Etienne Geoffroy Saint-Hilaire are the natural tribute paid to those precursors who not only believed in evolution, although their proofs of it were very inadequate, but also published their belief and thereby influenced their successors, including Darwin himself.

It is curious that Darwin did not include the name of his own grandfather Erasmus Darwin, whose works he had read and rejected, a fact which has laid Darwin open to the reproach of ingratitude to his grandfather. *Zoonomia,* in which Erasmus Darwin set forth his belief in evolution and attempted to account for it, was first read by Darwin before he embarked in the *Beagle* and while he still firmly adhered to theological orthodoxy, and this may be why, as he said, it had no effect on his mind. When he read it again ten or fifteen years later after he had convinced himself of the truth of evolution by his own observations, he had become a ruthlessly objective critic, and this may be why *Zoonomia* then disappointed him grievously, "the proportion of speculation being so large to the facts given." Later, when he wrote his *Autobiography,* Darwin admitted that the hearing rather early in his life of Erasmus Darwin's views on evolution maintained and praised, as they were by Robert Edmund Grant, probably favoured his own adoption of similar views though in different form. Erasmus Darwin and Grant must therefore be included among the factors that led Darwin to believe in evolution. It is difficult to know if the same can be said of Buffon, who was on Darwin's reading list,[11] and put forward evolutionary ideas in 1749 but withdrew them, or of Edward Blythe,[12] who in 1837 toyed with the idea of the common descent of different species but immediately and deliberately rejected it.

There were, however, some other men of whom Darwin never heard who speculated in favour of the idea that species might be transmuted into other species. Among these was Montesquieu, author of the *Esprit des Lois,* who, as early as 1721, thought[13] that reports of the existence in Java of "monkeys with bats' wings [flying lemurs] convinced my feeling that the difference between species of animals can increase every day, and diminish in the same way, and that there were in the beginning very few species, which have multiplied since." He continued, "I am persuaded that species change and vary extraordinarily, that some are lost and new ones formed." This was the application of the principle of gradation, erroneous as now realized but magnificent for his time, to a possible passage from bats through flying lemurs to monkeys.

Another of these men was Maupertuis, who in the middle of the eighteenth century attributed the almost infinite diversity of animals to transmutation of species, brought about by fortuitous variation.[14] Yet another was Diderot,[15] who took up and elaborated, while for diplomatic reasons pretending to reject it, a view put forward anonymously by Maupertuis under the pseudonym of Baumann,[16] according to which there was originally one animal, the prototype of all the others that were produced by Nature through lengthening, shortening, transforming, and multiplying certain organs.

Coming to more recent times, there was a Swiss from the Grisons, Alexander Moritzi, who concluded that species were transmuted from other species, and published his views at Soleure in 1842, completely ignored.[17]

Darwin knew nothing of the work of these men, who exerted no influence on him at all, but the accident of publication or of the failure of their views to be known to their successors should not stand in the way of the credit that is due them. It must be remembered that Darwin himself had no influence on Alfred Russel Wallace, who independently arrived at the same conclusions as himself. They were precursors on whose shoulders neither Darwin nor Wallace stood. It may be left to the humanists to select a term with which to describe this goodly company of voices crying in the wilderness.

After the *Origin of Species* was published in 1859, it seems that in the general ignorance and obscurantism that then prevailed, some readers reproached Darwin with attributing to himself the discovery of the fact of evolution, and this led him, on 18 January 1860, to write a letter[18] to Baden Powell which sets out his case and introduces Darwin's claim to what he did discover. He wrote: "No educated person, not even the most ignorant, could suppose that I meant to arrogate to myself the origination of the doctrine that species had not been independently created." This is in line with Darwin's note of 1838 quoted above. He went on to say: "The only novelty in my work is the attempt to explain *how* species became modified, and to a certain extent how the theory of descent explains certain large classes of facts; and in these respects I received no assistance from my predecessors." This is Darwin's claim to independent originality in propounding the principle of natural selection of heritable variation as the automatic mechanism that causes adaptations to arise and become improved, and evolution to occur. This claim is substantiated by the Notebooks on Transmutation of Species which record the train of Darwin's thoughts during the formative period from July, 1837, until July, 1839.

A close study of these Notebooks shows that the idea of natural selection, acting differentially on inadequate and adequate adaptation to the environment in which the species was living, occurred to him in July, 1837, because it is clearly set out in his First Notebook:[19] "With respect to extinction we can easily see that variety of ostrich Petise [*Rhea darwinii*] may not be well adapted, and thus perish out, or on the other hand like Orpheus [the mocking bird] being favourable, many might be produced. This requires principle that the permanent varieties produced by confined breeding and changing circumstances are continued and produce according to the adaptation of such circumstances, and therefore, that death of species is a consequence . . . of non-adaptation of circumstances." This is a clear recognition of the fact that varieties are adapted to their environments, and that if ill-adapted they are extinguished, whereas if well-adapted they flourish and multiply.

Another passage[20] from his First Notebook shows that Darwin had clearly gasped the importance of ecological niches to which organisms must be adapted if they are to survive: "I cannot for a moment doubt but what Cetacea and Phocea [whales and seals] now replace Saurians of Secondary epoch." They have taken their places in those ecological niches. The penalties of inadequate adaptation and the importance of heritable variation are seen in the following passage[21] from the Second Notebook, written before July, 1838: "Changes in structure being necessarily excessively slow they become firmly embedded in the constitution . . . . The constitution being hereditary and fixed, certain physical changes [in the environment] at last become unfit [for the organisms], the animal cannot change quick enough and perishes." This is a recognition of the fact, for which Darwin constantly acknowledged his indebtedness to Charles Lyell, that geographical and climatic conditions never remain the same.

The ingredients of the theory of natural selection of heritable variation, producing adaptation of organisms to their changing ecological niches, were therefore in Darwin's hands before he ever opened Malthus's *Essay on Population,* which he did, as he said, "for amusement," on 28 September 1838. In it he found one tooth for the cogwheels of his argument, and he immediately wrote a note from which the passage which struck him in Malthus's book[22] can be identified. It ran: "It may safely be pronounced, therefore, that the population, when unchecked, goes on doubling itself every twenty-five years, or increases in a geometrical ratio." The effect of this passage on Darwin's mind can be seen vividly in pages from his Notebooks which have only recently come to light, for Darwin cut out of his Notebooks those pages which he wanted to use when writing his large work, of which the *Origin of Species* was an abstract. They have now been found, and deposited in the University Library, Cambridge, by Sir Robin Darwin. The note[23] written by Darwin on 28 September 1838 in his abbreviated style, now first revealed in full, was as follows:

We ought to be far from wondering of changes in numbers of species from small changes in nature of locality. Even the energetic language of Decandolle does not convey the warring of the species as inference from Malthus—increase of brutes must be prevented solely by positive checks, excepting that famine may stop desire. In nature production does not increase whilst no check prevail but the positive check of famine and consequently death. . . . Population is increase at geometrical ratio in *far shorter* time than 25 years—yet until the one sentence of Malthus no one clearly perceived the great check amongst men—there is spring, like food used for other purposes as wheat for making brandy. Even a *few* years plenty makes population in men increase and an *ordinary* crop causes a dearth. Take Europe on an average every species must have same number killed year with year by hawks, by cold etc.—even one species of hawk decreasing in number must affect instantaneously all the rest. The final cause of all this wedging must be to sort out proper structure and adapt it to changes— to do that for form which Malthus shows is the final effect (by means however of volition) of this populousness on the energy of man. One may say there is a force like a hundred thousand wedges trying [to] force every kind of adapted structure into the gaps in the oeconomy of nature, or rather forming gaps by thrusting out weaker ones.

Here at last is the answer to the question, so often asked, what exactly it was that Darwin owed to Malthus. It was not the idea of evolution, or natural selection, or unlimited heritable variation, or the balance of nature, or adaptation to ecological niches, or changes in the conditions of the environment, for Malthus knew nothing of these and Darwin had grasped them already. It was the inevitability of mortality as a result of increase in numbers, which Malthus predicted for the human race, that Darwin, using De Candolle's war of nature, applied to species of plants and animals in nature. It provided him with a quantitative concept of the pressure at which natural selection must act, by ramming favourable variations into available ecological niches, and by evicting unfavourable variations from their niches so that they perished. It was a small and simple point, unrelated to Malthus's main conclusion that man was socially unimprovable; and it is the height of irony that this simple point enabled Darwin to show that it formed part of the mechanism whereby the adaptations of plants and animals to their environments were improved. Its simplicity led Huxley to want to kick himself for not having thought of it.

In his later years, when he wrote his *Autobiography,* Darwin laid so much stress on the effect that this point in Malthus's book had had on him[24] that he misled his readers into thinking that it was from Malthus that he had derived the idea of natural selection of heritable variation, which, as just shown, was not the case. The question therefore arises whether Malthus, on whose shoulder Darwin had a fleeting, unexpected and unintended foothold, can be regarded as one of Darwin's precursors.

Clearly not. As L. Z. Freedman and Anne Roe have remarked,[25] Darwin made an "analogical leap" from Malthus's argument to his own, and some expression other than precursor is required to describe a man whose work makes a contribution without his knowing it to another who uses it in a direction diametrically opposed to the intentions of that work.

Although Darwin, with his complete lack of historical sense, did not know it, Malthus was not acknowledged as the sole discoverer of the principle of population pressure. Hazlitt[26] reproached him for stealing the thunder from Robert Wallace, and other precursors in this field were Sir William Petty and Benjamin Franklin. Nor is Malthus's principle as applied to man unreservedly acceptable, because no limit has been set to the increase that human ingenuity and determination might attain in the matter of human food supplies with the help of new techniques. For the sparrow and the mouse, on the other hand, the principle holds. Here, therefore, is a paradoxical situation where a link in Malthus's fallacious argument has become a link in a valid argument by Darwin. This was not the first time that an approach to truth by a zigzag course was envisaged. Pandulph said:[27]

> The truth is then most done not doing it.
> The better act of purposes mistook
> Is to mistake again; though indirect,
> Yet indirection thereby grows direct,
> And falsehood falsehood cures . . .

That Darwin should have thought out the principle of natural selection and used it to explain the origin and improvement of adaptations, resulting in evolution and eventually in the origin of new species from old ones when the new ones ceased to be fertile with the old ones, does not imply that nobody else had thought of the struggle for existence, a principle that is basic to natural selection. Conway Zirkle has drawn up an impressive list[28] of such persons, from Empedocles and Lucretius for whom the survival of the fitter implied a kind of natural selection; but none of them used this principle to account for the transmutation of species, a possibility that did not occur to them, although some, like Maupertuis, Diderot, and David Hume, realized that the struggle for existence might be an alternative to teleological explanations of adaptation.

Before Darwin and Wallace, only two men, so far as is known, grasped the idea that natural selection could be an efficient cause of evolution, William Charles Wells[29] and Patrick Matthew;[30] but their publications received no attention, and neither was qualified to support his speculations with evidence or to generalize their application. Wells and Matthew therefore are further examples of precursors who made no mark.

Some difficulty attaches to the evaluation of the position to be assigned to two other men who knew of the struggle for existence and used it to support their arguments that evolution could not have occurred. One of these was Lyell, who in 1832, at a time when he firmly rejected the possibility of evolution, used the struggle for existence to explain the extinction of species. This was a concept that on theological grounds had been anathema to John Wesley and Thomas Jefferson, who denied that extinction of God's creations had ever occurred, but which Cuvier had shown to be inescapable. Lyell referred[31] to "the certain doom of a species less fitted to struggle with some new condition in a region which it previously inhabited, and where it has to contend with more vigorous species." Darwin had himself found extinct animals.

Even more difficult is the case of the second man, Edward Blyth, who in 1837 described the results to be expected in species that showed variability when exposed to sharp-eyed predators.[32] If the behaviour or the colour of these variants departed ever so little from the type of the species, by failing to match the natural background, or in vigilance, or by straying away from the appointed habitat, such variants would fall victims to their predators by the natural interplay of causes which, in Blyth's words, "destroyed all that deviate from their normal or healthy condition, or which occur away from their proper or suitable locality." These causes therefore "tend to limit the geographical range of species, and to maintain their pristine character without blemish or decay to their remotest posterity." So Blyth used natural selection to prove that species were immutable and that they had been specially created in the areas allotted to them.

Dr. Loren Eiseley, who brought to light Blyth's paper in which this argument is developed, has reproached Darwin for failing to acknowledge a debt to Blyth.[33] Darwin had high admiration for the excellent naturalist that Blyth was, he undoubtedly knew of Blyth's works, and frequently referred to him in his Notebooks and in his later book on *Variation in Animals and Plants under Domestication,* but, understandably, he never referred to Blyth's argument that the struggle for existence made evolution impossible. The questions may therefore be asked where Blyth stands in the pageant of precursors, whether Darwin owed him a debt, and if so what it was. The implication is that it was from Blyth that Darwin derived the principle that he elaborated into that of natural selection as a cause of evolution. This can be disproved, for Blyth's paper was published in 1837, whereas in 1832 Darwin had already read Lyell's *Principles of Geology* where De Candolle's words on the war of nature are quoted.[34] The idea of the struggle for existence had long been common property, as just explained. It can be found in the books of Erasmus Darwin, William Paley, and Lamarck among many others. Could it be that in this respect Blyth served not as a shoulder to stand on to see further forward, but as a scarecrow, an inducement to look precisely in the opposite direction? It would have been a delicate matter to acknowledge such a debt.

What is at issue here is the mystery of the creative processes in the mind and of the origin of an idea. Professor T. Dobzhansky, who has interested himself in this problem,[35] is of the opinion that conscious thinking processes are not wholly free from subconscious components, and that the creative activity of even the greatest minds does not always follow canons of logic. Probably the worst person to have asked how Darwin's flash occurred to him would have been Darwin himself, and there is proof of this in his *Autobiography,* where he lays misleading emphasis on his debt to Malthus. It will probably not be possible to get closer to Darwin's thoughts on 28 September 1838 than the contents of the excised pages from his Notebooks quoted above, which show that present in his mind, and perhaps at the back of it, were the ideas of inevitable climatic change, geographical isolation, heritable variation, adaptation to ecological niches, the struggle for existence, and extinction. It required only the forcefully presented idea of inevitable mortality for all the pieces in the jigsaw puzzle to take meaningful shape, as a result of a semi-conscious exercise in integration involving many terms, on that fateful day. None of these ideas was new, but their combination was.

Turning now to the second giant of biology, Mendel, his circumstances were completely different, for it is possible to show that he stood on nobody's shoulders at all.[36] He began breeding peas in 1854 and started crossing different varieties in 1856 in experiments[37] which he continued for eight years until 1863, although he probably owed a debt to his physics teachers in Vienna, A. von Ettinghausen and C. Doppler (of "Doppler effect" fame), not for anything in biology, but for instilling in him an interest in mathematical puzzles and problems. Experiments on plant hybridization had been undertaken before him by Joseph Gottlieb Koelreuter, Carl Friedrich von Gaertner, William Herbert, Henri Lecoq, and Max Wichura, whom Mendel mentioned; but their results were chaotic, inconsistent, and contradictory. The reasons for this were that the parent plants that they chose for their crosses were either of different species or of varieties differing in many characters; the questions from which they started were complex, such as whether sterility in a hybrid was the fault of the seed-parent or the pollen-parent, whether either parent was responsible for the characters of different specified parts of the plant offspring, and which parent had prepotency; and they failed either to count the different kinds of offspring or to follow the inheritance of their characters through successive generations. Mendel avoided all these errors by selecting parents that differed in only one character, and by following the mode of inheritance through several generations with numerical results that he expressed in ratios.

Mendel explained these results on a few simple assumptions: that characters were controlled by particles, atoms of heredity that are received by offspring from their parents in pairs, one particle of each pair from each parent; that the particles never contaminate one another; that when it comes to making germ-cells each member of each pair separates cleanly, or segregates from its partner so that no germ-cell contains more than one member from each pair; that germ-cells containing different particles are formed in equal numbers; and that all germ-cells have equal chances of fertilizing other germ-cells. These assumptions have been confirmed in every detail, and the only item to add is that the particles, or genes as they are now called, from time to time undergo spontaneous changes known as mutations, after which they continue in their changed state until they mutate again.

A curious feature of the numerical results of Mendel's experiments is that they imply that he knew what results to expect before he made the experiments. This follows from the statistical analysis of these results by Sir Ronald Fisher, who showed[38] that in some of Mendel's crosses the expected results, although logically defensible, did not allow for the corrections which the theory of probability requires when the numbers of individuals involved in the experiments are as small as those with which Mendel worked. Yet it was the results that Mendel expected, not the results that he should have expected, that he obtained. There seems to be no escape from the conclusion that his assistant and his gardener knew what he expected and, in all honesty but innocence, were biased towards obtaining it. This is no implication of deliberate falsification, for enthusiastic amateurs are all too prone to give an experiment the benefit of the doubt, when there is doubt, about material difficult to diagnose or imperfect, which is then rejected as so many spoilt voting-papers. Whoever was responsible may indeed be regarded as a great benefactor to science, by making the significance of the results easy to recognize. Polonius would have said:[39]

> Your bait of falsehood takes this carp of truth;
> And thus do we of wisdom and of reach,
> With windlasses, and with assays of bias,
> By indirections find directions out.

There is, however, a much deeper and more important implication to be derived from these facts, which is that Mendel must have thought out his system of particulate inheritance as an abstract idea, an exercise in mathematics before he subjected it to experimental tests in his breeding experiments. This was the mark of genius. Fisher has shown that the assumptions underlying a particulate system of inheritance are so simple that they could have been deduced *a priori* by anyone interested in solving mathematical puzzles, and Mendel is known to have had such an interest. This is the evidence for the claim that Mendel had no precursors at all to help him in his discovery of a principle on which is founded the whole science of genetics, the ramifications of which in other fields are now so many that it can be regarded as at the centre of science.

As in the case of natural selection, hindsight and bibliographic erudition have revealed men whose work can now be recognized as falling into line with the system of particulate inheritance. Jean-Antoine Colladon[40] in 1822 reported to a scientific society in Geneva the results of breeding grey and white mice, when he obtained only grey and white mice and no intermediates among the offspring as far as the third generation. This refusal of the characters to blend was regarded by Colladon as evidence that grey and white mice were different species, a view which was rightly opposed by De Candolle. The explanation is, of course, that grey and white are controlled by a single pair of genes, grey dominant to white, so that, if the greys are hybrids, segregation and recombination of genes can lead only to the production of grey and white offspring. As Colladon's paper was never published, and knowledge of it is confined to the manuscript proceedings of the society, his final conclusions are not known, but for all the importance of his experiments he can hardly be regarded as having anticipated Mendel's law of segregation. His work was in all probability unknown to Mendel when the latter started his experiments on peas, and this is a pity because at one stage Mendel himself bred mice.

Augustin Sageret in 1826 published[41] his experiments of crossing musk melons with cantaloups. He used parent plants the characters of which could be contrasted in pairs, yellow or white flesh, smooth or wrinkled skin, sweet or acid taste, and so on. He observed that the offspring showed no fusion of characters and that some were dominant over others, but here again no clear-cut principle of particulate inheritance emerged, and Mendel did not know of his work.

With Charles Naudin, whose results of crossing species or varieties of plants were published[42] in 1863, there is more difficulty in assigning a place. Attempts have been made to equate him with Mendel and to speak of the Naudin-Mendel laws, because Naudin observed reversion of his hybrids to their parental types; but he attributed such reversion to a disjunction in the hybrid of the "specific essences" of the two parental types en bloc.[43] This is a very different thing from the independent segregation of every pair of genes which is the basis of Mendel's system of particulate inheritance. Even more serious is that Naudin allowed for the possibility that in some germ-cells the disjunction of the "specific essences" of the parental types might not take place and that such germ-cells might themselves be hybrid, and that was how he explained different degrees of reversion: "The fertilization of a non-disjoined ovule by a pollen-grain disjoined in one parental direction or the other would give a quadroon hybrid; and as disjunctions, in pollen-grains and in ovules, can occur to all extents, recombinations will be produced which chance alone determines [translated from the French, p. 194]." This was in effect a provision for the notion of "blending" inheritance, and it disqualifies Naudin from the line of possible precursors of Mendel who, in any case, had not heard of this work when he made his experiments.

When Mendel's work was first restored to the light of day in 1900 after thirty-five years of almost (but not quite) complete neglect, his had been a voice crying in the wilderness, so that Carl Correns, Erik von Tschermak, and Hugo de Vries, who all independently obtained the same results, owed him nothing. Biologists then found themselves in a world where the two giants of the nineteenth century were made to confront each other in opposition. In neither case was his work fully understood. Mendelian geneticists claimed that their genes, which originated by mutation and produced sudden wide changes, were the only source of heritable variation and arose ready-made without any selection at all; they therefore rejected the Darwinian selectionists' contention that evolution was the result of selection working on small variations channelled in the direction of improvement of adaptations. The Darwinian selectionists for their part objected that the mutations which the geneticists waved at them involved wide changes and were almost always deleterious or pathological, and that, as mutation was a random event uncorrelated with the environment, it was utterly incapable of accounting for the origin and improvement of adaptation. Any biologist who started on his studies in the first two decades of this century will recall the chaos that reigned in his science, and the animosity that prevailed between the two schools, which took on some of the characters of the boat race because the Mendelian banner was flown by William Bateson in one place and the Darwinian banner by Edward Poulton in another. If Gilbert and Sullivan had then been alive, they would have found pleasant material in this situation. This antagonism was in a sense analogous to that between the upholders of the corpuscular and the undulatory theories of light, but with this difference—that the biological tangle has been completely resolved by the work of a man who in the opinion of many was among the greatest men of science of this century, Sir Ronald Fisher.

Fisher started with his feet firmly on the shoulders of Mendel and on those of Mendel's successor Thomas Hunt Morgan, whose great work on the fruit fly not only confirmed Mendel's principles in every detail, and showed that genes are carried in linear order in the chromosomes, but also imposed respect for a branch of science which has sometimes been called drosophilosophy. Before describing Fisher's analysis of the prickly problem, it must be recalled that experiments had shown that some genes and characters were dominant in a hybrid and others recessive. Fisher observed that the majority of mutations were not only recessive but deleterious, and he was led to the idea that they were recessive *because* they were deleterious. Further, if in the course of evolution genes have one by one been replaced by new mutant genes, the prevailing rule that the normal wild-type genes are dominant to their mutant partners must mean that the wild-type genes have *become* dominant to them. This hypothesis was accessible to experiment and was confirmed. Mutant genes become recessive if they are deleterious and become dominant if they are advantageous, for there are some advantageous mutations.

The next question was to discover how this effect was produced. It involved a scrutiny of the old view that a given gene was invariably linked to "its" character. Experiment showed that this was not the case; the effects of a gene in controlling a character are subject to the control of all the other genes in the gene-complex of the organism. The gene-complex is like a kaleidoscope which changes as it is reshuffled as a result of segregation and recombination at every generation. But in this process there is a high rate of mortality. Those gene-complexes that bring out the worst features of a deleterious new mutant gene kill their possessor, whereas those gene-complexes that attenuate the deleterious effects of such genes, by making them recessive and masking their effects, survive. This is nothing other than selection exerted at the level of the genes, and one of the most striking aspects of Fisher's work is that it led him to find incontrovertible evidence of selection at the heart of genetics.

This conclusion, confirmed by experiment,[44] means that the effects of genes under the control of the gene-complex can produce gradual and small changes in the characters of the organism, and improve adaptation. That particulate inheritance is discontinuous is no reason why visible changes in organisms should be discontinuous; they are not. All the obstacles between the geneticist and selectionist points of view melted like snow before this illuminating synthesis, and it is now recognized that the system of Mendelian genetics provides exactly the mechanism required for characters of organisms to change slowly and improve their adaptation under the influence of selection, as Darwinian theory suggested.

There are other important corollaries of Fisher's synthesis, such as the demonstration[45] that selection, *not* mutation, determines the speed and the direction of evolution, a fact which has been confirmed in palaeontological studies[46] by George G. Simpson. Even now, and particularly on the continent of Europe, the view is sometimes heard that "mutationism" is the theory of the cause of evolution upheld by the so-called Anglo-Saxons. Such views are self-condemned as forty years out of date.

The firm stance that Fisher established on the shoulders of both Darwin and Mendel is eloquently reflected in the title of his great classic, *The Genetical Theory of Natural Selection*,[47] which shines not only as a landmark in the history of science but also as an example of the way in which apparently irreconcilable points of view can be harmonized and integrated as a result of seminal ideas and further research. After their battle, Tweedledum and Tweedledee have sat down to dinner together.

In this brief sketch an attempt has been made to trace the epoch-making ideas of Darwin, Mendel, and Fisher, three great men of science; but there is no reason to think that the processes involved are different in other fields of intellectual endeavour, which makes it only the more regrettable that our great cultural heritage should have become split into different streams. In the sciences as in the liberal arts the mental processes are the same, and the use of imagination. As William Whewell saw,[48] the elementary or generative act in scientific discovery is an idea the consequences of which can then be tested. There is no such thing as *the* scientific method. Observation and experiment can be applied to natural phenomena, and only they can then lead to the discovery of natural laws, but they are not likely to produce great results unless ideas, imagination, intuition, and even inspiration are behind them.

In Great Britain, since about a hundred years ago, science has meant the natural sciences, and this limitation is doubtless due to the material benefits conferred by applications of physics, chemistry, biology, and medicine, compared with which the advantages that have accrued from philosophy are uncertain. Ruskin struggled hard to resist this limitation in the use of the word, and in 1875 he argued[49] that "there is a science of Morals, a science of History, a science of Grammar, a science of Music, and a science of Painting; and all these are quite

beyond comparison higher fields for human intellect, and require accuracies of intenser observation, than either chemistry, electricity, or
geology." It is not surprising that his advocacy defeated his object.
In France, where the split in culture is less deep and Buffon and
Pasteur were members of the Académie Française, epigraphy, numismatics, bibliography, palaeography, genealogy, and linguistics rank as
sciences, because they are studied by "scientific" methods of observation
and verification, and they benefit from the loosening of the purse-
strings which the magic word "science" induces in grant-giving
authorities, even if they cannot discover any laws of Nature. An example is provided by a recent discovery on the coast of Brittany.[50] In
1960 a man of Brest collected seaweed to manure his garden from a
pile that had been blown on the shore by gales. In it, encrusted by the
seaweed, he found a coin that turned out to be a gold stater minted at
Cyrene just after the death of Alexander the Great, about 322 B.C.
The shore, near Ushant, is one of the most dangerous at the entrance
to the Channel, and the conclusion is inescapable that the coin came
from a ship wrecked at that place. Greek seaborne expeditions in those
waters were then particularly rare, because of the close watch which the
hostile Carthaginians maintained over the Strait of Gibraltar; but it so
happened that Pytheas, a Greek from Marseilles, slipped through after
321 B.C. and sailed up the Channel. There can be little doubt that the
hapless ship was one of his. Numismatics gives further information,
because Marseilles minted silver coins only, and for an expedition of
this kind into the unknown, Pytheas would have required to provide
himself with gold, which the friendly city of Cyrene could supply.
This fascinating research ranks in France as "scientific" although it has
led to the discovery of no general principle.

The difference between scientists and those who pursue the humanities does not reside so much in their methods as in the materials on
which they work. Observation and experiment have been applied by
man to men for three thousand years with little success in discovering
general principles of universal validity. Observation and experiment
have been applied by man to natural phenomena for three hundred
years and have resulted in resounding success in extracting general
principles of universal validity and application. The difference lies in
the fact that natural phenomena show a regularity which lends itself
to rigorous analysis without asking any man's opinion, and leads to

broad general principles such as the laws of motion, gravitation, thermo-dynamics, natural selection, and genetics. The actions of man endowed with conscious purpose interefere with the workings of Nature so that he and the results of his desires and activities, which are subject to human preferences, become unpredictable and irreducible to simple or-der and principle, in spite of what Plato, Rousseau, and Marx have written. But this difference, which is the difficulty against which politicians, philosophers, and theologians strive, must not be allowed to obscure the fundamental uniformity of human mental processes.

Painters, musicians, and poets have also made a practice of standing on the shoulders of their predecessors, sometimes without acknowledg-ment. The chain-links of inspiration in movements and schools of art and music are there for all to see and hear. The study[51] of the works of Erasmus Darwin and of Shelley show how the latter frequently de-rived not only the sentiments but also the technique and even the words of his verses from his predecessor; but he is forgiven because his ideas, imagination, intuition, and inspiration effected such improvements that he reached the highest level of art.

Sometimes the releasing factor is as unexpected as Malthus's effect on Darwin. A young Pole was sitting on the Furka Pass in Switzer-land in 1873 when an English tourist went by. Joseph Conrad was arguing with his tutor because he wanted to go to sea, and the tutor was getting the better of the argument when the Englishman, en-veloped no doubt in an aura of "Rule Britannia," tipped the scale. He smiled at Conrad. The tutor gave up the struggle. Conrad went to sea.[52]

Even more curious was the source of inspiration of Jean Giono, a rustic, lyrical pantheist prose-poet from Manosque, whose advent was hailed by André Gide as that of a Virgil newly risen in Provence, re-garded by many as one of the greatest living French novelists. Giono has explained what started him on a career so unexpected in a bank-clerk son of a cobbler in a small provincial town. The spark was fired by the opening words of Kipling's *Jungle Book:* "It was seven o'clock of a very warm evening in the Seeonee hills when Father Wolf woke up from his day's rest." Giono said: "It was this simple phrase that started it all off. I felt convinced that I, also, was capable of writing, and of going on in my own way [translated from the French]."[53]

In this mystery of the creative processes of the mind, there is little difference between scientists and poets. Coleridge was deeply interested in this, as shown by his words:[54] "The imagination . . . the true inward creatrix, instantly out of the chaos of elements or shattered fragments of memory, puts together some form to fit it." This form arises out of "A Vision in a Dream." As a result of his analysis of the factors at work in the composition of Coleridge's poems, J. L. Lowes came to the conclusion that Coleridge's Notebook "gives us some inkling of the vast, diffused, and amorphous nebula out of which, like asteroids, the poems leaped. It makes posible in other words, at least a divination of that thronging and shadowy mid-region of consciousness which is the womb of the creative energy."[55] The same might be said of the workings of the mind of a great man of science. Chemical factors, internal such as hormones, or external such as absinthe, opium, mescalin, or snuff, may play a part. Schiller kept rotten apples in the drawer of his desk because of their smell.

It has been said, perhaps facetiously, that to copy from one author is plagiarism, but to copy from a hundred authors is research. It would be nice to know at what number a reprehensible practice becomes respectable; but it should be remembered that, if subconscious processes are at work, what might appear to be plagiarism to a reader could be involuntary in an author and even repudiated by him in good faith.

It comes to this, that imagination, as Coleridge also said,[56] "dissolves, diffuses, dissipates in order to recreate." In men of genius it has a unifying, integrating, and shaping spirit, and it is this shape that gives its character to the creation, whether poem or scientific hypothesis; but it was not created out of nothing. In the physical world, shaping can only be obtained by expenditure of energy, whether at the molecular level or that of Henry Moore. This is what physicists mean when they say that entropy tends to a maximum, for the natural condition of equilibrium is chaos, the state of maximum probability, imposed by the second law of thermodynamics. In the world of ideas, they take shape in the human mind without the specific expenditure of any physical energy that can be detected, and this is perhaps why creations of the mind give the appearance of true creations, something produced out of nothing. A comparable state of affairs was revealed by Emerson when he remarked[57] that a beautiful face, without any exertion, had the power of giving great pleasure. There seems to be no physical balance-sheet here.

In the history of the world, there have been many examples of what has come to be called thought-control, imposed by spiritual or temporal authorities, the aim of which has been to prevent anyone from climbing onto unauthorized shoulders in case he should see further. Such measures have met with varying degrees of success; but what no authority has ever been able to control is the origin of ideas. They are unpredictable and their effects are incalculable. They arise with an indeterminacy comparable to that which characterizes the mutation of one gene per locus per generation in half a million, or the disintegration of one radioactive atom with a frequency consonant with the life of the element. Newton's famous statement with which this study began should therefore be respectfully rewritten. If he was able to see further than most men, it was not only by standing on the shoulders of giants, but by having ideas, imagination and inspiration of his own that enabled him to make use of his privileged position. After all, a pygmy raised even to the summit of Everest would see only with the eyes and mind of a pygmy, which means that shoulders are all very well, but men of genius can see vast horizons because they are who they are.

The Greek verb *poiein* means "to make," and it appears in English scientific language in hæmopoiesis, formation of blood. *Poiein* has also given the noun *poietes,* he who creates, whose mind is a garden where ideas grow. It is translated "poet" and has become restricted to writers of verse, but its real meaning applies equally well to artists, composers, mathematicians and men of science; so there is really only one world after all.

CHAPTER

2

The Origins of Darwin's Ideas on Evolution and Natural Selection

The Wilkins Lecture delivered before the Royal Society, December 7, 1961. From the *Proceedings of the Royal Society, B,* volume 155, pp. 321–338, 1962.

For the origins of the ideas that led Darwin to the theories of evolution and natural selection, the classical source of information is his *Autobiography*.[1] That splendid document was written in 1876, forty years after the critical period in question and when Darwin was sixty-seven years old. That is not a great age by modern standards, but in his case it was towards the close of a life of hard work, constantly interrupted and handicapped by an illness which was always distressing, most probably due to the South American form of trypanosomiasis known as Chagas's disease, contracted during excursions ashore from the *Beagle*, as Professor Saul Adler,[2] F.R.S. has shown. The difficulty in evaluating autobiographies of old men lies not so much in the fact that they forget, as in the fact that the passage of time and the gradual assimilation of new ideas, together with hindsight, present a picture different from the day-to-day record of the progress of those ideas when they were prized out of facts or surged ahead out of inspirations.

Few works would seem to have had so unimpeachable a birth-certificate as that which Gibbon[3] in his Memoirs gave to the *Decline and Fall of the Roman Empire.* "In my Journal," he wrote, "the place and moment of conception are recorded; the fifteenth of October, 1764, in the close of evening, as I sat musing in the Church of the Zoccolanti or Franciscan Fryars, while they were singing Vespers in the Temple of Jupiter on the ruins of the Capitol." But Gibbon's Journal[4] contains nothing of the kind, and two other versions of his Memoirs omit mention of it. Professor Georges Bonnard[5] has shown that these cele-brated passages were a subsequent reconstruction in Gibbon's mind of a long-drawn-out process that could not be dated to a single day. With-out any intention of impugning the veracity of Darwin's *Autobiography,* it will not be without profit to scrutinize it closely in the light of con-temporary documents.

The critical apparatus for the study of the origins of Darwin's ideas comprises several documents covering the period of the voyage of the *Beagle* and the years immediately following his return to England. First come his Diary[6] and those entries in his travel Pocket-books[7] that are dated, because his parsimoniousness in the use of paper led him to use old notebooks and make later entries in them. These precious documents have been edited and published by Lady Barlow.

Next come the Ornithological Notes,[8] which Lady Barlow has found to contain an early assemblage of his observations on birds used in his *Journal of Researches*[9] describing the voyage of the *Beagle.* The *Jour-nal of Researches* was written between January and June, 1837, and the Ornithological Notes therefore antedate the *Journal of Researches.*

The perspicacity of Dr. Sydney Smith[10] has enabled him to recog-nize marginal comments of great importance in Darwin's copy of the fifth edition of Lyell's *Principles of Geology,* which was published in March, 1837, probably the date of Darwin's entries. In July of the same year, 1837, Darwin "opened his First Notebook on Transmutation of Species," which was followed by three more.[11] In August, 1838, shortly before his engagement to be married, he drew up a Journal[12] in which he summarized his work up to that date. Subsequently, from May to June, 1842, he allowed himself "the satisfaction of writing a very brief abstract" of his theory in pencil,[13] and this was enlarged during the summer of 1844 into an essay of 230 pages.[14] It is common knowledge that in 1856 Darwin started to write an exhaustive treatise on evolution, that on 18 June 1858 he received from Alfred Russel Wallace a complete outline of his own theory,[15] and that he thereupon started to prepare what he called an "abstract," which the world knows as *On the Origin of Species*, published on 24 November 1859.

The Original Construction of Darwin's Theory of Evolution

On the recognition of the fact of evolution itself, the relevant passage of the *Autobiography*[16] reads: "During the voyage of the *Beagle* I had been deeply impressed by discovering in the Pampean formation great fossil animals covered with armour like that on the existing armadillos; secondly, by the manner in which closely allied animals replace one another in proceeding southwards over the Continent; and thirdly, by the South American character of most of the productions of the Galapagos archipelago, and more especially by the manner in which they differ slightly on each island of the group."

Four principles are here involved. The first is the succession of types connecting extinct fossils with living representatives. He found[17] his first fossil, *Megatherium,* on 23 September 1832, and on 24 November wrote[18] to John Stevens Henslow, "I have been very lucky with fossil bones. . . . I found a large surface of the osseous polygonal plates, which 'late observations' . . . have shown to belong to the megatherium. Immediately I saw them I thought they must belong to an enormous armadillo, living species of which genus are so abundant here."[18]   The relevant passage in the *Journal of Researches*[19] reads, "The most important result of this discovery, is the confirmation of the law that existing animals have a close relation in form with extinct species."

The second principle relates to representative species, by which is meant the fact that adjacent areas of a continent are inhabited by different but related species which take each other's place. This was forcibly borne in on Darwin in December, 1833, when he not only saw but ate the Petise (*Rhea darwinii*), before realizing that it was the southern Patagonian representative of the more northerly *R. americana*.[20]   From the start, his Ornithological Notes are filled with searches for species differentiation in the light of changes of habitat and the existence of physical barriers between the ranges of species.

The third principle concerns the resemblance of the inhabitants of oceanic islands to those of the nearest continental mainland. Darwin's Pocket-book under the date 18 September 1835, within two days of his first landing on the Galapagos, carries the entry, "I certainly recognize South America in Ornithology."[21]

The fourth principle arises from the differences between the inhabitants of the different islands of the Galapagos archipelago. The physical conditions of these islands are identical, and, as Dr. Loren Eiseley[22] has pointed out, it was with utter astonishment that Darwin realized shortly before his departure that he should have made separate collections from each island. In the *Journal of Researches*[23] he wrote, "Unfortunately, I was not aware of these facts till my collection was nearly completed: it never occurred to me, that the production of islands only a few miles apart, and placed under the same physical conditions, would be dissimilar." In spite of this, his Ornithological Notes show that the number of specimens listed as coming from different islands is considerable.

That this was the most vivid impression made on him by the entire voyage may be seen from the entry in his Ornithological Notes written probably at some date in the latter half of 1836 on the voyage home: "When I recollect the fact, that from the form of the body, shape of scale and general size, the Spaniards can at once pronounce from which Island any tortoise may have been brought: when I see these Islands in sight of each other and possessed of but a scanty stock of animals, tenanted by these birds but slightly differing in structure and filling the same place in Nature, I must suspect they are only varieties. The only fact of a similar kind of which I am aware is the constant asserted difference between the wolf-like Fox of East and West Falkland Islands. If there is the slightest foundation for these remarks, the Zoology of Archipelagoes will be well worth examining; for such facts would undermine the stability of species."[24]

With these words, Darwin served notice on the old order. His mind moved steadily; by the time he landed in England he must have abandoned belief in the fixity of species, and by March, 1837, he was well on the way to his theory of evolution. That date not only accords with the known dates of the work on which he was engaged, but is confirmed from two other sources. The first of these is the marginal annotations that he made in his copy of the fifth edition of Lyell's

Principles of Geology. The essential requirements for evolution are that there should be variation, that the variation should be conserved, that there should be no limit to the extent of that variation, and that the more favoured variants in a particular habitat should be preserved. Darwin's comments show, as Dr. Sydney Smith[25] has pointed out, that by March, 1837, he had realized the importance and the truths of the first three of these four propositions. To Lyell's statement, "When the change of situation that they [organisms] can endure is great," Darwin added the word "or small," showing that he already understood the importance of small variations. To Lyell's statement that "peculiarities of form, structure, and instinct, are transmissible to the offspring," Darwin added the phrase "with no tendency to go back," showing that he appreciated the importance of heritable variation. To Lyell's assertion of "indefinite divergence, either in the way of improvement or deterioration being prevented," Darwin entered the protest: "if this were true *adios* theory," showing that he already had a theory for the transmutation of species and that he set no limits to the extent of variation, which was a great and original step on his part.

Although Darwin's *Journal of Researches* was not published until August, 1839, he had finished writing it by June, 1837, as is known from his letter to W. D. Fox of July, 1837. The *Journal of Researches* was therefore written during the critical period when Darwin's views on evolution were taking shape, but his natural caution prevented him from broaching them in that volume. Nevertheless, there is one passage that shows clearly that he was not afraid of admitting that evolution might have occurred. It is on page 400 where he deals with the differences between the flora and fauna on the western and eastern sides of the Cordillera of the Andes, saying, "Unless we suppose the same species to have been created in two different countries, we ought not to expect any closer similarity between the organic beings on opposite sides of the Andes, than on shores separated by a broad strait of the sea." Here Darwin added a footnote: "This is merely an illustration of the admirable laws first laid down by Mr Lyell of the geographical distribution of animals as influenced by geological changes. The whole reasoning, of course, is founded on the assumption of the immutability of species. Otherwise the changes might be considered as superinduced by different circumstances in the two regions during a length of time." Later, Darwin likened disbelief in the immutability of species to "confessing a murder"; here, he was already prepared to admit that this very "murder" might be contemplated.

Then, in his *Journal*[26] in August, 1838, he wrote: "In July [1837] opened first note-book on transmutation of species. Had been greatly struck from about month of previous March on character of South American fossils, and species on Galapagos Archipelago. These facts origin (especially latter) of all my views."

The First Notebook on Transmutation of Species[27] shows not only how much thought Darwin had put into the problem since his return from the voyage of the *Beagle*, but also how much foreshortening his recollections had undergone by the time he wrote his *Autobiography* in 1876. If anyone expected that the Notebook would begin with the fourfold experience in South America and the Galapagos described in the *Autobiography*, he would be surprised because the Notebook attacks the subject from a different angle altogether.

In the book *Zoonomia*[28] by his grandfather Erasmus Darwin, Darwin hit upon the following passage: "This paternal offspring of vegetables, I mean their buds and bulbs, is attended with a very curious circumstance: and that is, that they exactly resemble their parents, as is observable in grafting fruit-trees, and the propagating flower-roots; whereas the seminal offspring of plants, being supplied with nutrient by the mother, is liable to perpetual variation." Under this bogus attribution of gender to the two methods of reproduction, asexual and sexual, lurks an important truth which Darwin noticed:[29] sexual reproduction results in variation, as we now know because it enables segregation and recombination of genes to take place, whereas the genetic make-up of the products of asexual reproduction is the same as that of the stocks from which they have come. It is also to be noticed that this observation has nothing to do with Erasmus Darwin's belief in transmutation of species on grounds which Darwin rejected because they lacked evidence.

Darwin already recognized "two kinds of varieties. One approaching to nature of monster, hereditary, other adaptation."[30] The former are now called mutations, the latter environmental modifications, but Darwin inclined to think that they could also become hereditary.

From this starting point, Darwin asks a question:[31] "With this tendency to vary by generation [that is, by sexual reproduction], why are species constant over whole country?" Answer:[31] because of "intermarriages partaking of characters of both parents." Here, straightaway, Darwin was brought up against his greatest difficulty, the then commonly accepted idea of "blending inheritance" which, in the absence of any experimental knowledge of genetics, supposed that the characters of offspring struck an average between those of the parents with the result that variation in a population would quickly be cancelled out.

Next comes Darwin's trump-card:[32] "separate a pair and place them on fresh island, it is very doubtful if they would remain constant." He went on:[33] "isolate species, especially with some change, probably vary quicker." In other words, isolation of a few organisms can protect their variation from being obliterated, and their offspring will differ from the original population. This passage is like a summing up of his Notes on the Cordillera, and it is difficult to be sure whether Darwin thought this out for himself, or whether he reflected the views of two other men to whom he refers later in his Notebook. One of these was Alexander von Humboldt, whose Personal Narrative of Travels greatly influenced Darwin. In that book Humboldt[34] had said: "The exclusion of all foreign mixtures contributes to perpetuate varieties, or the aberrations from a common standard." The other was Leopold von Buch,[35] a geologist with whose work Darwin was familiar because for a long time geology was his favourite subject. Darwin's note[36] reads, "Von Buch distinctly states that permanent varieties become species."

In July, 1837, therefore, Darwin was in possession of a consistent theory of evolution to which, from then on, he always referred as "my theory." He immediately proceeded to test it. "As we thus believe species vary, in changing climate we ought to find representative species; this we do in South America."[37]

On the succession of types, Darwin wrote,[38] "Propagation [that is, the descent of species from other species, not by special creation] explains why modern animals [are the] same types as extinct," and he continues[39] "according to my view, in South America parent of all armadilloes might be brother to Megatherium—uncle now dead."

Of the resemblance of inhabitants of oceanic islands to those of the nearest continent, Darwin notes,[40] "remembering Lyell's arguments of transportal, islands near continents might have some species same as nearest land, which were late arrivals, others old ones of which none [of] same kind had in [the] interval arrived might have grown altered. Hence the types would be of the continent, though species all different. Two cases as Galapagos and Juan Fernandes." Lyell's *Principles of Geology*, volume 2, which Darwin received at Montevideo[41] on 26 October 1832, contains a relevant passage:[42] "Quadrupeds found on islands situated near the continents, generally form a part of the stock of animals belonging to the adjacent main land." Lyell then quoted from Charles Pritchard's *Physical History of Mankind*: "but small islands remote from continents are in general altogether destitute of land quadrupeds, except such as appear to have been conveyed to them by men. Kerguelen's Land, Juan Fernandez, the Galapagos, and the Isles de Lobos, are examples of this fact." Lyell's imagination was more fertile in admitting methods "of transportal" across the sea, and it was to these that Darwin was indebted.

On the differences between the inhabitants of different islands of the same archipelago, Darwin's Notebook says,[43] "According to this view, animals on separate islands ought to become different if kept long enough apart, with slightly different circumstances. Now Galapagos tortoises, mocking birds, Falkland fox, Chiloe fox. English and Irish Hare." The words "long enough" show that he had grasped the importance of limitless time for evolution to take place.

The representative species that Darwin had found in South America, particularly the two rheas with distinct characters in adjoining areas, at first made him think that "if one species does change into another it must be per saltum—or species may perish . . .—not gradation."[44] This note in his Pocket-book is echoed in his First Notebook:[45] "We must suppose the change is effected at once . . . every grade in that case it seems is not produced?" ending with a query of uncertainty. Later on this view is given up and he speaks of "forms slightly favoured,"[46] showing that he had appreciated the importance of minute variations.

The value of Darwin's Notebooks on Transmutation of Species lies not only in the information which they give on the way Darwin's ideas formed in his mind, but also in the indication of the provenance of those ideas of which he made use. For the notes on the differences between the inhabitants of adjacent islands and on the succession of types, he quoted nobody. The former of these principles, forced on him by his experiences in the Galapagos Islands, was clearly his own discovery. The idea of the succession of types, however, subsequently became a subject of controversy and deserves further attention.

All that was meant by the succession of types was that in some areas species had become extinct, as was proved by their fossil remains, and that other but similar species were alive. It implied nothing about the way in which the types succeeded one another, which might have been by special creation, or, as Darwin believed, by transmutation. In a paper[47] which Darwin read on 3 May 1837 he attributed priority of discovery of the principle of succession of types to Edward Wedlake Brayley's remarks on South American fossils, made in 1831. In the *Origin of Species* he attributed it to William Clift's researches on Australian fossils, published[48] likewise in 1831. In the first edition of the *Journal of Researches*,[49] published in 1839, Darwin stated the principle clearly and regarded his discoveries as confirming it. In the second edition,[50] published in 1845, there was a striking passage with well-placed emphasis for the benefit of those, if there were any, who appreciated the significance of the word "hereafter": "This wonderful relationship on the same continent between the dead and the living will, I do not doubt hereafter throw more light on the appearance of organic beings on our earth, and their disappearance from it, than any other class of facts." Richard Owen claimed priority for himself in his *On the Nature of Limbs*, published in 1849. Darwin claimed no priority for it, although he appears to have worked it out for himself; but its significance for him may be seen in his words to Charles Lyell: "this law, with the Galapagos distribution, first turned my mind on the origin of species."[51]

If species have arisen by transmutation, it means that they have ancestors in common. Community of descent was implicit in the ideas of Erasmus Darwin and of Lamarck, and Darwin had some difficulty in deciding whether Geoffroy Saint-Hilaire entertained it or not.[52] In the same year Darwin opened his Notebook, Edward Blyth[53] asked the question, "May not then, a large proportion of what are called species have descended from a common parentage?" and immediately rejected this possibility because if it were true, "we should seek in vain for those constant and invariable distinctions [between species] which are found to obtain." In other words, Blyth rejected evolution by (rightly) rejecting the very reason for which Lamarck accepted it, namely, the erroneous supposition that species could grade insensibly into one another. Blyth is mentioned in Darwin's Notebooks, but not on this point unless it was on pages which he excised to write his later works.

Dr. Eiseley[54] has regretted Darwin's neglect of Blyth, but it is an exercise of some nicety to think how he would have recorded his indebtedness to a man whose conclusions were the negation of what he was trying to prove.

By July, 1837, Darwin had conceived "his theory," and it is not necessary to follow him in his search for further facts to establish or refute it, because it already calls for comment on a number of points. In the first place, it is not a static description of evolution as a series of historic events, but a dynamic causal explanation of those events, in so far as he was able to provide one before he had grasped the principle of natural selection. That was to come a year later. Meanwhile, with the material at his disposal, his theory was logical and justifiable, although in the light of present knowledge it can be seen to contain a fallacy, because interbreeding within a population does not quash variation. Interbreeding keeps the members of a population in the same species but does not necessarily keep the species unchanged. In fact, Darwin's position appeared to him to be more difficult than it actually was. The theory as outlined in the Notebooks is traceable through the Sketch that he wrote in 1842 and the Essay[55] in 1844, but after that he altered it. In order to appreciate this evolution in Darwin's mind, it is necessary to turn to the origin of his ideas on natural selection.

The Construction of the Theory of Natural Selection

The relevant passage in the *Autobiography*[56] reads, "I soon perceived that selection was the keystone of man's success in making useful races of animals and plants. But how selection could be applied to organisms living in a state of nature remained for some time a mystery to me. In October 1838, that is, fifteen months after I had begun my systematic enquiry, I happened to read for amusement Malthus on *Population,* and being well prepared to appreciate the struggle for existence which everywhere goes on from long-continued observation of the habits of animals and plants, it at once struck me that under these circumstances favourable variations would tend to be preserved, and unfavourable ones to be destroyed. The result of this would be the formation of new species. Here, then, I had at last got a theory by which to work."

It is not generally realized that this famous sentence is another example of the foreshortening of old men's memories and has led to one of the great paradoxes in the history of science. How is it possible that Darwin, the apostle of biological evolution, could have derived anything from Malthus, who believed that social change was impossible? Malthus is little read nowadays, and some clarification of the point is required.

The story begins with the speculations of the great French philosophers of the eighteenth century. Montesquieu, Maupertuis, Diderot, and for a time Buffon until he was called to heel by the Sorbonne, entertained the idea that species could change. Even Jean Jacques Rousseau believed that man had degenerated since the golden age as a result of the pernicious effects of civilization, a view which at least admitted the possibility of retrogressive change. But in Condorcet,[57] the French Revolution threw into prominence a man who argued eloquently in favour of the perfectibility of mankind. In England these views were echoed by William Godwin,[58] and the revolutionary ideals of progress established a bridgehead in this island, where they were rejected with increasing horror and revulsion by most Englishmen as the excesses of the French Revolution grew worse. On the theological side, an attempt to stem the tide of the ungodly was made by William Paley in a book[59] that exerted a great influence on Darwin, albeit in a direction which its author could not foresee. On the sociological plane, the champion of the old order was Malthus.[60]

Starting from the proposition that the potential rate of reproduction of man was geometrical, whereas his supplies of food could increase only in arithmetical progression, Malthus propounded his principle that if in spite of famines and epidemics population increased too fast, those who could least well afford the necessities of life were doomed to misery and death. On the other hand, if the checks to the increase in numbers of a population were artificial and too effective, there would be no competition or compulsion to work and the results would be misery from the effects of immorality, sloth and idleness. In either case, mankind could not improve, and as Malthus regarded such variation as cultivated plants and domestic animals showed to be strictly limited, evolution, another subversive notion which Lamarck had recently brewed out of the witches' cauldron of the French Revolution, was impossible. How could Darwin have owed anything to the views of such a Jeremiah? Darwin himself must have sensed the paradox, for he was careful to dissociate himself from "Malthusian views" of limited variation.[61]

The answer is complicated by the fact that Malthus's object in writing his book was not scientific but political, and much of the opposition to him was, and is, political. It was devastatingly voiced by his contemporaries. For instance, William Hazlitt:[62] "why does Mr Malthus practise his demonstrations on the poor only? Why are they to have a perfect system of rights and duties prescribed to them? I do not see why they alone should be put to live on these metaphysical board-wages, why . . . it should be meat and drink to them, more than to others to do the will of God." Shelley:[63] "War, vice, and misery are undeniably bad, they embrace all that we can conceive of the temporal and eternal evil. Are we to be told that these are remedyless, because the earth would, in case of their remedy, be overstocked?" And Byron:[64] "Notwithstanding Malthus tells that were it not for Battle, Murder, and Sudden Death, we should be overstocked, I think we have latterly had a redundance of these national benefits." These comments are worth quoting because Darwin, to the end of his days, never understood the political overtones which, whether he liked it or not, were attached to his work. To Carl Heinrich von Scherzer he wrote:[65] "what a foolish idea seems to prevail in Germany on the connexion between Socialism and Evolution through Natural Selection."

In fact, the paradox of Darwin's debt to Malthus is resolved because Darwin did not owe his theory of natural selection of variations to Malthus at all, but thought it out for himself. This is known from the fact that he had succeeded in getting the idea of natural selection clear in his mind before February, 1838, while it was on 28 September 1838 that he read[66] Malthus's *Essay on the Principle of Population*. Extracts from his Notebooks establish this beyond doubt.

First of all it is important to notice Darwin's appreciation of the significance for his problem of artificial selection as practised by man in producing different cultivated plants and races of domestic animals. It appears clearly in an entry[67] dated 7 September 1838: "I was struck looking at the Indian cattle with Bump, together with Bison of some resemblance as if the 'variation in one was analogous to specific character of other species in genus.'" In other words, the magnitude of the differences between domestic breeds of cattle produced by artificial selection, exemplified in the hump of Indian cattle, was comparable to the magnitude of the differences between the two species of cattle and of bison.

The importance of adaptation to the environment for survival is shown in the following:[68] "With respect to extinction we can easily see that variety of ostrich Petise [a species now known as *Rhea darwinii*] may not be well adapted, and thus perish out, or on the other hand . . . being favourable, many might be produced." Then, after consideration of changes resulting in the formation of new species, he wrote:[69] "All this agrees well with my views of those forms slightly favoured getting the upper hand and forming species." Here, clearly expressed, is the theory of evolution by natural selection of favourable variations. Darwin himself realized his own priority in this matter, for when he looked over his Notebooks in 1856 he added in pencil:[70] "Towards close I first thought of selection owing to struggle."

As Darwin had reached this position before he ever read Malthus, what did he owe to Malthus? Nothing but a general demonstration in quantitative terms of the inevitable toll of mortality exacted from every species of plant and animal, and this provided the sanctions for his theory of natural selection. As Darwin later[71] wrote to Wallace, "I came to the conclusion that selection was the principle of change from the study of domesticated productions; and then, reading Malthus, I saw at once how to apply this principle." He had already grasped the principle of natural selection and had seen how it could result in unlimited change away from the ancestral type and the production of new species; but he had not recognized how nature enforced this principle until he had read Malthus.

As the theory of natural selection was and is regarded as Darwin's own, personal, and original contribution to science, it is important to consider possible sources from which he might have derived the idea. Basic to natural selection is the struggle for existence. This was common property. It pierces rather ashamedly through the pious lucubrations of Paley.[72] It figures in the works of Erasmus Darwin,[73] Lamarck[74] and Lyell,[75] it was elevated by Augustin Pyrame de Candolle[76] to the status of the war of nature, and Darwin had observed it for himself:[77] "It is difficult to believe in the dreadful but quiet war of organic beings going on in the peaceful woods and smiling fields."

The notion of selection involves not only variation, but the dependence of the fate of each individual plant and animal on its own characters and qualities. In artificial selection it was the common practice of every horticulturist and stock-breeder. Its application to conditions in nature was made by Lyell,[78] who used it to explain extinction: "A faint image of the certain doom of a species less fitted to struggle with some new condition in a region which it previously inhabited, and where it has to contend with a more vigorous species, is presented by the extirpation of savage tribes of man by the advancing colony of some civilized nation." But at the time when Lyell wrote those lines he firmly rejected evolution.

Edward Blyth gave a description[79] of the results of variation in species preyed upon by sharp-eyed predators. If the behaviour or colour of the variant departs ever so little from the type of the species, by failing in vigilance or in matching its natural background or in straying away from it, such variants will fall victim to the predator by the natural interplay of causes which remove "all that deviate from their normal or healthy condition, or which occur away from their proper or suitable locality," and thereby "tend to limit the geographical range of species, and to maintain their pristine characters without blemish or decay to their remotest posterity." In other words, like Lyell, Blyth used natural selection to prove that species were immutable, that evolution was impossible and that species had been specially created in the areas allotted to them.

If this were true, then it should follow that species were by now perfectly adapted to the environments for which they had been created, and that no intruders from elsewhere could be better adapted to those environments. But as Dr. Eiseley has said,[80] "Darwin had brought back with him the memories of foreign weeds invading the new world, of introduced animals overrunning the indigenous products of oceanic islands," and his Notebook[81] shows his appreciation of the importance of imperfect adaptation. It meant that all species had not reached a steady state, and this must have been his own conclusion.

For what Darwin called "my theory," referring only to the fact of evolution before he had formulated the principle of natural selection, he made little claim to originality. "Scarcely any novelty in my theory, only slight differences, the opinion of many people in conversation."[82] Early in September, 1838, he wrote:[83] "Seeing what Von Buch, Humboldt, Geoffroy-Saint-Hilaire, and Lamarck have written I pretend to no originality of ideas (though I arrived at them quite independently and have used them since); the line of proof and reducing facts to law only merit if merit there be in following work."

Later on, when his theory of evolution by natural selection was complete, he wrote[84] to Baden Powell: "No educated person, not even the most ignorant, could suppose that I meant to arrogate to myself the origination of the doctrine that species had not been independently created. The only novelty in my work is the attempt to explain *how* species became modified, and to a certain extent how the theory of descent explains certain large classes of facts; and in these respects I received no assistance from my predecessors."

It was not long before Darwin and Wallace were informed that William Charles Wells[85] and Patrick Matthew[86] were predecessors who had actually published the principle of natural selection in obscure places where their works remained completely unnoticed until Darwin and Wallace reawakened interest in the subject. These works show that neither Wells nor Matthew had any appreciation of the magnitude of the principle on which he had stumbled, or any competence to work it out. Of greater interest is the fact, recently revealed by Sir Edward Bailey,[87] that the unpublished notebooks of James Hutton, the father of uniformitarianism, contain a good description of the principle of natural selection.

The most important result of the theory of natural selection was that it substituted a simple automatic mechanism for what had previously been regarded as design, divine or providential, to account for the production of the adaptations, often called beautiful adaptations, that plants and animals show in respect of their environments. Immediately the idea of design is discarded, the notion of fortuitousness of variation takes its place, and as Dr. Eiseley[88] has remarked, the origin of such a notion in Darwin's mind is important. That he was deeply interested in the question of design is known not only from his letters to his friends and his *Autobiography,* but also from the final chapter of his book on *Variation.*[89] In the *Origin of Species* the problem is not raised directly but pervades the entire book. It emerges clearly in such phrases[90] as "can we doubt that individuals having any advantage, however slight, over others, would have the best chance of surviving and of procreating their kind? On the other hand, we may feel sure that any variation in the least degree injurious would be rigidly destroyed." There can be no question of design as between such variations, but only of fortuitousness.

The First Notebook (in 1837) contains an entry which probably sowed the seed of fortuitousness in Darwin's mind, even before he had grasped the principle of natural selection or had a use for it. Frédéric Cuvier,[91] brother of the great palaeontologist, published an essay on the domestication of mammals in which he wrote, "we could only produce domestic individuals and not races, without the occurrence of one of the most general laws of life—the transmission of a fortuitous modification into a durable form." After quoting these words, Darwin added,[92] cryptically, "I take higher grounds and say life is short for this object."

There is no doubt about Darwin's meaning in passages of his Fourth Notebook. William Herbert[93] had remarked that "no plant becomes acclimated under our observation, except by crossing with a hardier variety, or by the accidental alteration of constitution in some particular seedling," on which Darwin[94] commented: "my principle being the destruction of all the less hardy ones and the preservation of *accidental* hardy seedlings." It enabled him to answer his own question when he wrote,[95] "Seeing the beautiful seed of a bull-rush I thought, surely no 'fortuitous' growth could have produced these innumerable seeds, yet if a seed were produced with infinitesimal advantage it would have better chance of being propagated and so and etc."

The Greater Variability of Large Populations

It is now time to return to Darwin's presentation of his case for evolution. While engaged on his large work, he was led in 1857 to consider the implications of some observations that can be traced to his Notebook of 1837. His attention was called[96] by the works of Humboldt[97] and Deshayes[98] to the fact that genera may differ in the number of species that they contain; and Fries[99] had shown that species belonging to genera that contained many species are more closely related to one another than are the species of genera containing few species. In his letters to his friends Hooker, Lubbock, and Asa Gray during 1857 and 1858, Darwin showed that these facts implied that variability was greater in species belonging to genera containing many species;[100] furthermore, that wide-ranging, much diffused, common species abounding in individuals vary most.[101] This conclusion, in turn, leads to the further one that species inhabiting large areas will be exposed to more severe competition than inhabitants of smaller areas and will reach higher stages of evolution in a given time.[102] This is why the centre of origin of the major groups of land-animals has lain in the largest land-mass, the Old World, from which emigrations have taken place to the ends of the habitable earth.

The principle of greater variability in larger populations is of such importance that it has been subjected to genetic analysis by Sir Ronald Fisher and Dr. E. B. Ford, who confirmed it.[103] It appears in the *Origin of Species*:[104] "in any limited country, the species which are the most common, that is abound most in individuals, and the species which are most widely diffused within their own country . . . oftenest give rise to varieties sufficiently well-marked to have been recorded in botanical works. Hence it is the most flourishing, or, as they may be called, the dominant species, those which range widely, are the most diffused in their own country, and are the most numerous in individuals, which oftenest produce well-marked varieties, or, as I would consider them, incipient species."

What has happened to the old argument developed in the Notebooks of 1837, the Sketch of 1842 and the Essay of 1844 to the effect that "if in any country or district all animals of one species be allowed freely to cross, any small tendency in them to vary will be constantly counteracted?"[105] This was where Darwin had started. The facts of the distribution of species and varieties had driven Darwin to believe that it was possible to overcome the resistance to change imposed by "blending inheritance" if variations were sufficiently numerous. This also had an effect on the interpretation of the importance of isolation, originally in Darwin's view a *sine qua non* for variation to persist. Now, in the *Origin of Species*,[106] isolation is still regarded as important in preventing interbreeding with the parent stock and in keeping habitats available for occupation. "If, however, an isolated area be very small, either from being surrounded by barriers, or from having very peculiar physical conditions, the total number of the inhabitants will be small; and this will retard the production of new species through natural selection, by decreasing the chances of favourable variation arising."[107]

When it is added that in the *Origin of Species*[108] variation is no longer invariably connected with the act of generation or sexual reproduction, because somatic variations in plants can be reproduced by cuttings, it will be seen that all three of the initial arguments on which Darwin had originally based his view in July, 1837—that variation depends exclusively on sexual reproduction, is obliterated by interbreeding, but protected by isolation—had been overthrown and replaced by the natural selection of fortuitous variations.

The Principle of Divergence

Darwin always attributed great importance to what he called his principle of divergence. In his *Autobiography*[109] he described it as "the tendency in organic beings descended from the same stock to divergence in character as they become modified. That they have diverged greatly is obvious from the manner in which species of all kinds can be classed under genera, genera under families, families under suborders, and so forth; and I can remember the very spot in the road, whilst in my carriage, when to my joy the solution occurred to me; and this was long after I had come to Down." From a letter to George Bentham in which Darwin wrote,[110] "I believe it was fifteen years after I began before I saw the meaning and cause of the divergence of the descendants of any one pair," this carriage ride must have been in 1852.

Darwin specified that he had not solved this problem when he wrote his Essay in 1844, and it has been the subject of some misunderstanding. Not only that Essay, but the Notebook of 1837 contains a splendid discussion of the principle of branching and sub-branching of the evolutionary tree. Darwin already knew all about this, and what he was referring to was not the fact of divergence but a causal explanation of how it occurs and how it increases. "How, then," he asked in the *Origin of Species*,[111] "does the lesser difference between varieties become augmented into the greater difference between species?" The problem was no longer one of branching or of splitting a species into two, but of widening the split. The solution, also given in the *Origin of Species*,[112] is that "The more diversified the descendants from any one species become in structure, constitution and habits, by so much will they be better enabled to seize on many and widely diversified places in the polity of nature." In other words, divergence is related to the existence of ecological niches.

As this subject touches the very foundations of the science of ecology, to which Darwin contributed so much, attention may be drawn to entries in his Notebooks on Transmutation of Species relating to it. On the existence of niches, he was already clear in 1837: "I cannot for a moment doubt but what Cetacea and Phocea now replace Saurians of [the] Secondary Epoch."[113] Even more apposite is his question on how a niche is entered: "When a species becomes rarer, as it progresses towards extermination, some of the species must increase in number— where then is the gap, for the new one to enter?"[114] Most enlightening of all is a long note made early in January, 1839: "The enormous number of animals in the world depends on their varied structure and complexity, hence as the forms became complicated, they opened fresh means of adding to their complexity; but yet there is no necessary tendency in the simple animals to become complicated, although all perhaps will have done so from the new relations caused by the advancing complexity of others."[115] Here Darwin showed that he had already realized the part that organisms themselves play in the ecological complex of factors which make up the environment of other organisms. As for the filling of niches he concludes, "I doubt not if the simplest animals could be destroyed, the more highly organized would soon be disorganized to fill their places."[116] All this he thought out for himself.

The Pattern of the History of Science

As a result of this study of the origins of Darwin's ideas on evolution and natural selection, it is clear that some were derived from his own observations and meditations and some from the works of other men. On the one hand, Erasmus Darwin and Lamarck believed in evolution but, lacking any notion of natural selection, were incapable of explaining satisfactorily how it occurred. On the other hand, Lyell and Blyth understood the action of natural selection but used it to prove that evolution could not occur. The ingredients out of which Darwin constructed his theory of evolution by natural selection were known to them, but they failed to see their significance, partly because they never tested the imaginary and non-existent link between Cuvier's doctrines of catastrophism and progressionism,[117] and partly because of the orientation of their minds toward theological orthodoxy. It was left to Darwin, who intended to become a clergyman, to repeat the trick of Columbus's egg, and it is no disparagement of his achievement that it was simple enough for Huxley[118] to exclaim, "How extremely stupid not to have thought of that."

A further example of a synthesis made out of facts known to others is Sir Ronald Fisher's demonstration[119] that far from being antagonistic and mutually exclusive, Darwinian selection and Mendelian genetics are complementary and indispensable to each other, and between them provide exactly what is required to explain the mechanism of evolution. It is capable of producing stability because it is based on genes that do not become contaminated, can be closely linked in a chromosome, and mutate seldom. It is also capable of producing change because its mechanism allows for segregation, recombination of genes, and "crossing-over" of chromosomes. Here it was William Bateson who missed the chance of making this synthesis by failing to recognize that mutations can have infinitesimal and cumulative effects producing gradual change, and by neglecting the possibility that selection of genes in the gene-complex plays a part in controlling the effects of mutations. The main evidence on which Fisher constructed his synthesis was accessible to Bateson, but his opposition to natural selection concealed its significance from him.

It will not be accounted impious to Darwin's memory if a comparable analysis is applied to him and the question is asked why he did not make Mendel's discovery. He knew of mutations or "sports" which arise suddenly and are inherited.[120] He knew of pure lines, obtainable by inbreeding.[121] He knew of what is now called segregation and described it clearly[122] in terms of visible characters, but not of factors. He recognized that "some characters refuse to blend, and are transmitted in an unmodified state either from both parents or from one."[123] "I know of a good many varieties, which must be so called, that will not blend or intermix, but produce offspring quite like either parent."[124] As an example, "I crossed the Painted Lady and Purple sweet peas, which are very differently coloured varieties, and got, even out of the same pod, both varieties perfect, but none intermediate."[125] He obtained[126] a fair approximation to a simple Mendelian 3 to 1 ratio after crossing the common snapdragon with the peloric form; the F_1 were all common, and of the F_2 the common forms numbered 88 to the peloric's 37. Here, in addition, was the phenomenon of dominance and the extraction of recessives from heterozygotes. He also knew of what are now called F_1 uniformity and F_2 variability which are tests for Mendelian inheritance: "When two well-marked races are crossed the offspring in the first generation take more or less after either parent or are quite intermediate between them, or rarely assume characters in some degree new. In the second and several succeeding generations, the offspring are generally found to vary exceedingly, one compared with another."[127]   Here, if only he could have realized it, was the complete, experimental disproof of "blending inheritance," the evidence for particulate inheritance, and the solution to his difficulty of finding an adequate source of variation.   It was all the more peculiar because in his hypothesis of pangenesis,[128] Darwin entertained the possibility of particles being responsible for heredity.   The answer to the puzzle is probably complex.   Crosses between breeds, now, but not then, known to differ in many genes, gave mongrels that appeared to blend, and Darwin was so imbued with the importance of correlation that it would have been difficult for him to conceive of characters as units.   There is also the hint given by Darwin himself when he wrote in his *Autobiography,*[129] "in after years I have deeply regretted that I did not proceed far enough at least to understand something of the great leading principles of mathematics; for men thus endowed seem to have an extra sense."[130]

Darwin's successors have sufficient reason to be grateful to him for what he did, even without this "extra sense."   Furthermore, his case, like the two others and many matters in this study, serves only to show the significance of a statement by A. N. Whitehead: "Everything of importance has already been said by someone who did not discover it." It is part of the pattern of the history of science.[131]

CHAPTER

3

Genetics:
The Centre of Science

Opening discourse at the Royal Society Symposium held for the Centenary of Mendel's first paper, given on March 10, 1965. From the *Proceedings of the Royal Society, B,* volume 164, pp. 154–166, 1966.

It is not often possible to pinpoint the origin of a whole new branch of science accurately in time and place, because, as Isaac Newton said, there are usually so many precursors on whose shoulders the successor stands and is thereby able to see further than they. But genetics is an exception, for it owes its origin to one man, Gregor Johann Mendel, who expounded its basic principles at Brno on 8 February and 8 March 1865.

If a precursor is a man who, at an earlier date, makes a discovery which his successor is able to expand into a general principle of universal validity, Mendel had no precursors. There were not wanting breeders who hybridized plants—Joseph Gottlieb Koelreuter, Carl Friedrich von Gaertner, and William Herbert, to mention only the chief names—but what they were studying was not really basic genetics at all. They wanted to know if sterility in a hybrid is the fault of the pollen-parent or the seed-parent, whether either parent could be held responsible for the characters of different specified regions of the plant, or which had prepotency over the characters of the hybrid. The parent races that they chose for their crossing experiments were either different species, or varieties differing in large numbers of characters, and the results which they obtained were chaotic, inconstant, and contradictory, and led to no general principles at all. This was the difference between previous attempts to study heredity, and the Mendelian revolution that resulted in genetics.

Charles Naudin has been claimed as a precursor of Mendel because in 1863 he envisaged the possibility of the "disjunction of characters" as a result of which the hybrid could produce offspring differing from itself and leading to reversion towards the parental types. But he attributed this effect to the "disjunction" of the "specific essences" of the original strains of the parents, temporarily united in the hybrid, and waiting in the germ-cells to be "disjoined" *en bloc*. In his hypothetical scheme, Naudin also allowed for germ-cells that failed to "disjoin" the "specific essences" of the parents but allowed them to remain combined in varying proportions, to account for different degrees of reversion to the parental types. In other words, as I have pointed out in greater detail on page 38, Naudin's scheme contained a built-in provision for the possibility of blending inheritance, and Naudin cannot be claimed as a precursor of Mendel.

Augustin Sageret has been hailed as another precursor. In 1826 he published his results of experimental crossing between musk melons and cantaloups, in which he noticed that his parent forms differed from one another in characters that could be contrasted in pairs: flesh white or yellow, seeds white or yellow, flavour acid or sweet. He observed that some of these characters were dominant over others and that the F_1 generation was uniform, and he concluded that a hybrid did not show fusion of parental characters, but a "distribution." This, however, was not equivalent to a discovery of segregation of unit-factors. At an even earlier date, in 1822, J.-A. Colladon observed what is now recognized as dominance when he crossed grey and white mice and found that their offspring were always either grey or white, but never intermediate. He continued these experiments as far as the third generation, and it is evident that what he was doing was to make back-crosses between heterozygous grey mice and homozygous recessive white mice; but the absence of blending, itself an important discovery, led him to conclude that grey mice and white mice were different species. Mendel knew nothing of any of these experiments.

Nothing is more dangerous than to invite that siren of history, hindsight, to read into old works conclusions which their authors did not demonstrate or enunciate, and there is little in any earlier work that forestalls Mendel's analysis of the problem into situations where parents differing in single pairs of visible character-differences at a time resulted, after crossing, in hybrid offspring in certain specified proportions. This constancy of characters of hybrids, as Mendel himself explained, was the starting point of his work. It also enabled him to postulate an hypothetical explanation of his results by supposing that the characters were each governed by particulate factors, that the factors from each parent segregated cleanly at the formation of the germ-cells in equal numbers, and that the chances of fertilization of germ-cells bearing one or other of the two different factors which thereby became recombined were equal in probability.

The statistical analysis of Mendel's numerical results, carried out by Sir Ronald Fisher, leads to the important conclusion that Mendel knew what proportions to expect when he made his experimental crosses. What this means is that he had thought out his scheme of particulate inheritance beforehand in his head, as an abstract and simple mathematical exercise, before he put it to the test. It was not an empirical discovery subsequently processed by induction into a scheme.

Expecting a distribution of $1:2:1$, or $3:1$ where one of the characters showed dominance, the results which Mendel obtained in the F_2 generations of his crosses, reduced to proportions as he, for the first time, reduced them, were striking: $2.96:1$; $3.01:1$; $2.84:1$; $2.95:1$; $3.14:1$; $3.18:1$; $2.907:1$. It may be asked why Fisher concluded that Mendel discovered his rules as a result of an idea, subsequently tested by deduction and experiment. The evidence is that in some cases Mendel's expectations, although logical, were not statistically correct for the small numbers of the samples with which he worked. In the case of simple monohybrid (involving a single pair of contrasting characters) crosses he found that in F_2 the dominant form was approximately three times as numerous as the recessive. His theory required that of the individuals of that dominant form so produced, one-third should be capable of breeding true (homozygotes) and two-thirds should be hybrids that did not breed true (heterozygotes) but segregated and gave offspring some with dominant and some with recessive characters. He therefore expected a 2:1 ratio of those two genotypes in the dominant phenotype of an F_2 generation. His method was to grow ten seeds from each of sixty plants to be tested, all showing the dominant form, thereby raising an F_3, and he obtained 399 plants that segregated into dominant and recessive offspring to 201 plants that showed no segregation. These figures, 399:201, are as near to the expected ratio of 2:1 as anyone could wish; but this result was too good to be true because, as Fisher showed, with samples of only ten seeds from each plant to be tested, some 6 per cent of the heterozygous plants would be expected to fail to show segregation and would give nothing but dominant offspring. This 6 per cent of plants would therefore be classified among the homozygotes, to which they do not belong. The expected ratio should have been, not 400 to 200, but 377.5 to 222.5. As just mentioned, the figures given by Mendel were 399 to 201. The same discrepancy between expectation, corrected for the small numbers used, and results is found in other figures given by Mendel, and Fisher was therefore driven to the conclusion that Mendel's expectations were known to his assistants. There is no question of attributing deliberate falsification to these assistants, but it is well known that enthusiastic amateurs are prone to give an experiment the benefit of the doubt and to bias the results unintentionally by discarding poor specimens and doubtful cases, and by making honest mistakes. The figures published by Mendel as a whole would be expected to be equalled or improved on once in 8,000 trials.

Fisher's conclusion that Mendel's work stemmed from an idea, worked out theoretically as a mathematical exercise, is supported by the extraordinarily thorough manner in which Mendel expressed his system in mathematical terms and in generalized form for universal application. He was able to state that, in crosses that involve one pair of factor-differences, the proportions of the genotypes in subsequent generations resulting from self-pollination are 2^n-1 homozygous dominants to 2 heterozygotes to 2^n-1 homozygous recessives where n is the number of generations. He was also able to provide formulae for calculating the number of recombinations and genotypes resulting from crosses involving more than one pair of factor-differences. If n is the number of pairs of factor-differences between the two parents, then 3^n is the number of genotypes produced in F_2, 4^n is the number of possible recombinations that make up those genotypes, and 2^n is the number of those that will be homozygous and breed true.

As Fisher said: "All the main characteristics of the Mendelian system flow from assumptions of particulate inheritance of the simplest character, and could have been deduced *a priori* had any one conceived it possible that the laws of inheritance could really be simple and definite." This is exactly what Mendel appears to have done. It not only adds to his stature as a genius, but shows how ideas can flash from the brows of men as well as of Zeus, and how irrelevant was and is so much of the talk of the supremacy of so-called Baconian methods of induction in the progress of science. Mendel had an idea, and it worked.

It is commonly held that Mendel's work, which was published in 1866, was ignored and re-discovered in 1900. This is only partly true. What happened in 1900 was that a few men, reacting against the Darwinian selectionist view that evolution had taken place by small and almost imperceptible steps, contended on the contrary that evolution took place by wide, marked, and discrete steps; and when H. de Vries, C. Correns, and E. von Tschermak obtained the same results as Mendel had, and found that Mendel had already published them, the clear-cut differences between phenotypes such as round and wrinkled peas, or tall and dwarf plants, were hailed as evidence in favour of saltatory evolution and of opposition to Darwin. Because heredity was found to be discontinuous, it was concluded wrongly that evolution also must have been discontinuous.

This use of a Mendelian stick with which to beat Darwin created such enthusiasm that the essential nature of Mendel's discovery was missed altogether, the significance of particulate inheritance. Not realizing that the wide distinctions between the phenotypes then known were due to the fact that they were the most easily detectable extremes of what is really a continuous series, it was asserted that species evolved into other species at one blow, by large mutations, without paying any attention at all to the problem of the origin and improvement of adaptation. Even more serious was the misuse of what was then thought to be the principles of genetics by the elaboration of programmes of eugenics, based on the supposition that there was an absolute and unalterable one-to-one relation of causality between a factor or gene and what was supposed to be "its" character, to which the possessor was regarded as irrevocably condemned by a dogma of scientific Calvinism, overreaching itself in a state of imperfect and incomplete knowledge, and in danger of becoming a travesty of science.

It is now realized that no character owes its existence to inheritance alone or to environmental factors alone, a point which seems to have been emphasized first by E. Ray Lankester and E. S. Goodrich. No character is either innate or acquired; all are both, but in varying degrees because the degree of penetrance that genes show can be very variable. It is important to recognize the width of the bracket set by the genes within which environmental factors can make the genotype produce variable phenotypes. Examples are provided by the Fuegians that Captain Fitzroy brought to England to teach them "Christianity and the use of tools." As Darwin wrote in his *Diary* for 6 February 1833, "in contradiction of what has often been stated, 3 years has been sufficient to change savages into as far as habits go, complete and voluntary Europeans."

The converse process of animalization of human beings may be seen in apparently well-authenticated cases (though sometimes doubted) of young children brought up by wild animals—bears, wolves, or leopards—studied by E. Bonnot de Condillac in the eighteenth century, J. M. J. Itard in 1807, and by Father J. A. L. Singh in the 1920's. T. Monod has recently described a case of an antelope child in West Africa. The animalized children walked on all fours and could not adopt the erect attitude, lapped their food, and were nocturnal in their habits. They howled like their foster-parents and could scarcely be made to understand or speak any words. Analogous results are shown in cases of children sequestrated by inhuman parents, studied by Kingsley Davis in 1939. What has, however, not been made clear, as G. de Morsier has pointed out, is whether these animalized children were neurologically normal *before* they became wild. Nevertheless, it can hardly be doubted that, as the painter Auguste Renoir said, "les parents font les enfants, mais après leur naissance" ("parents make children, but after they are born"). Experiments on young rhesus monkeys by M. K. and H. F. Harlow provide striking evidence of how deprivation in early life modifies the phenotype.

Perhaps the most remarkable case of the effect of environment in modifying a phenotype is that of Mrs. Clare Kipps's sparrow Clarence, a day-old fledgling extruded from its nest and reared by her in her home. He developed two real bird songs while accompanying her as she played on the piano, walked with alternate steps instead of hopping, loved to lie on his back and have his tummy stroked, played, scolded, bullied, acted, had a fetishism for his foster-mother's hairpins, and showed devoted affection. None of these characters would have developed had he been reared in his nest, and instead of becoming a stupid and limited little bird, he developed into a personality with more character than is shown by many dogs. Mrs. Kipps repeated this experiment with a nest-fledged young sparrow, Timmy, who also showed great character, but this character was quite different from that of Clarence, which must be attributed to a difference in genotype between these two sparrows. Another example of a "humanized" animal was Elsa the lioness, described by Joy Adamson and seen by Sir Julian Huxley.

Of course, when conditions during the development of successive generations are constant, genetics tells; Hapsburg lips remain Hapsburg, Bourbon noses remain Bourbon noses. A learned genealogist once received a visit from a man of old family and peculiar name. When the genealogist heard it, he immediately asked his visitor, "Have you got webbed feet?" and the man had.

This is the occasion to give credit that is due to those geneticists who have come to be called the "early Mendelians." Plants had furnished the material studied by Mendel himself, and by De Vries, Correns, and Tschermak; but L. Cuénot in France, and W. Bateson and R. C. Punnett in Britain, showed that Mendel's principles also applied to animals, which was an immense step, the significance of which is still perhaps underestimated by those who are more struck by the differences than by the fundamental resemblances between plants and animals.

Bateson further performed the great service of introducing into the young and growing subject a standardized nomenclature which has been universally accepted, including such household terms as "allelomorph" (now commonly abbreviated to allele), for genes controlling characters which can be exchanged for one another, "homozygote," and "heterozygote." To W. Johannsen is due the concept, demonstration, and term of "pure-line," the word "gene," and the indispensable distinction between "genotype" (an individual defined by its genetic constitution as inherited from its parents) and "phenotype" (an individual defined by its appearance, the result of interplay between its genetic constitution and the environment during its development), together with the terms used to connote them. While on the subject of nomenclature, "phenocopy" (similarity due to environmental change) is due to R. Goldschmidt, "genocopy" (similarity due to genetic change) to P. B. Medawar, and the definition of "genetic polymorphism" to E. B. Ford.

Two developments of fundamental importance in the history of genetics must be given the honour that is their due. Towards the end of the nineteenth century, partly as a result of the progress in microscopy due to the introduction of Abbe's improvements of the instrument and the invention of the coverslip, W. Flemming discovered chromosomes, and A. Weismann advanced the idea that they were the bearers of his "determinants." As is well known, Weismann's theory of development had to be abandoned as a result of the discoveries in experimental embryology made by W. Roux, who showed that the various blastomeres in early stages of cleavage of the fertilized egg received qualitatively identical nuclear legacies from their parent cells; but Weismann's identification of chromosomes as bearers of hereditary factors was inspired. In 1902, W. S. Sutton made the specific suggestion that the behaviour of chromosomes at the formation of germ-cells provided exactly the mechanism needed for the distribution of Mendel's factors. This was followed by the magnificent ocean of experiments on *Drosophila* by T. H. Morgan and his colleagues A. H. Sturtevant, C. B. Bridges, and H. J. Muller, which established beyond any possibility of doubt that Mendel's principles of heredity were correct and that his factors, Morgan's genes, were carried in linear order in the chromosomes. This fundamental advance carried with it the explanation of "coupling" and "repulsion" as the results of linkage and crossing-over.

What Morgan and his men demonstrated with their breeding-bottles received independent confirmation from cytological studies, especially by C. D. Darlington, M. J. D. White, R. Matthey, and others, who worked out not only the modalities of chromosome behaviour, replication of strands, inversions, translocations, chiasmata and other details which provide a firm physical basis for genetical phenomena, but also the manner in which the chromosome mechanism itself has evolved, the evolution of an evolutionary mechanism. The result has been a triumph, for no less an expression is adequate to describe the success with which maps of genes in chromosomes have been drawn, and their accuracy confirmed by independent genetical and cytological evidence. This view of the genes is so near an approximation to the truth that it can be accepted for all practical purposes except for the fine structure of the genetic material; for, as S. Benzer has shown, the unit of genetic recombination, the *recon,* the unit of mutation, the *muton,* and the unit of function are not coextensive, and the concept of the *cistron* has been introduced as the unit of function which may contain many units of recombination, while the unit of mutation may be larger or smaller.

This is also the occasion to refer to a special case of genetics which has provided answers to one of the most fundamental questions in all biology, the determination of sex. It has been studied by both geneticists and cytologists and may also justly be regarded as an example of a biological triumph. It has turned out to be a "mechanism" in the true sense and, among the numerous contributors to its elucidation, mention must be made of L. Doncaster, C. B. Bridges, and R. Goldschmidt. It also solved the problem of sex-linked inheritance.

There remains to be considered the significance of Mendel's chief contribution to science: the particulate nature of inheritance which was not fully understood in its significance until Fisher's work was published in 1930. It means, in the first place, that, instead of becoming diluted at each generation as had been thought on the notion of "blending inheritance," variance is conserved. Formulae had already been worked out, by G. H. Hardy and W. Weinberg, which express the distribution of genes in a population quantitatively, thereby laying the foundation of population genetics. The conservation of variance means that the chief difficulty is removed from the problem of the origin of heritable variation, Darwin's greatest puzzle, because the recombinations of genes provide for an enormous supply of variation, greater than can actually be realized in a population. Genes change by means of sudden, random, non-adaptive changes known as mutations, and it is because of past mutations that members of pairs of allelic genes differ from each other; but the rate of mutation is estimated to be low. On a rough average only one in half a million genes per locus on chromosomes per generation mutate, and it is no paradox to say that, from the point of view of continuing evolution, mutation is of comparatively little importance. It is recombination of existing mutants that provides the supply of heritable variation for evolution, and the master of ceremonies in that process is found to be the very thing that was rejected of men when Mendel's paper was first rescued from oblivion in 1900, selection.

In view of the broadsides that early geneticists had fired at natural selection, there is something ironical in the story of Fisher's setting out and finding incontrovertible evidence for selection at the heart of genetics. It happened in this way. Fisher noticed that, of 221 mutants described in *Drosophila,* 208 had recessive effects and 13 intermediate in character. This was an uneven and lop-sided distribution. Next, he noted that in series of multiple alleles, while the wild-type allele was always dominant, the other alleles never showed dominance over one another. Further, dominance was no essential part of the hereditary mechanism, for many crosses obeyed Mendel's laws without showing any dominance at all. Additional facts were that gene novelties are usually recessive, and that recessive characters are usually deleterious. From all this he was led to the idea that dominance and recessiveness of the characters that they controlled were not fundamental properties of genes at all, but were themselves the result of evolution. Considering further the fact that, if in the course of evolution genes have, one by one, been replaced by mutant alleles, the prevailing rule that the wild-type gene is dominant to its alleles can hold only if the wild-type gene has *become* dominant to them. What is at issue here is the relation between a gene and the characters that it controls (which can be numerous), or between genotype and phenotype.

How is the phenotypic effect of a gene modified? The answer was found in the study of the offspring of individuals carrying mutants inbred for many generations. It is then observed that the effect of the gene in question has been modified and reduced. But, if that gene is placed back again into the original strain and gene complex in which it mutated, it shows the same old effect. This means that the effects of a gene are modified by the other genes of the gene complex, which, during the course of inbreeding, has had its other heterozygous alleles shuffled about until a gene complex has been produced in which the gene in question is subdued. In other words, the gene has *become* recessive, and this is what has happened to mutants with deleterious effects. Conversely, other genes, particularly in changed environments, may have their effects enhanced by a reshuffling of the gene complex; in other words they have *become* dominant, and this is what happens to beneficial genes and is the reason why the genes in the wild type are dominant. This hypothesis has been put to direct experimental test for the first time in wild material by E. B. Ford, who showed that, by selecting in opposite directions, the same gene can be made to become dominant in one selection line and recessive in another. Similar results were subsequently obtained by other workers.

This is the proof of the efficacy of selection at the heart of genetics, and there is one more important thing to add. Mathematical analysis of the effects of selection has provided a picture which shows that mutation is powerless to control the direction and speed of evolution, whereas selection is all-powerful. Since, as just mentioned, mutants under the conditions in which they mutated are generally deleterious and reduced to a recessive state or even further, evolution cannot be caused by any agency which might be invoked to control the direction of mutation. Only the opportunistic, wasteful, blind, and blundering action of natural selection, working on the heritable variation provided by recombination of alleles resulting from previous mutation, agrees with all the facts and is sufficient to explain the mechanism of evolution.

It is curious that the fundamental importance of Fisher's work and its implications seems to have been largely ignored in continental western Europe, where there are biologists who still object vehemently to what they call the "Neo-Darwinian theories" which they reproach their "Anglo-Saxon" colleagues for holding. But the "Neo-Darwinian theories" as described by such biologists (and rightly rejected by them) are only forms of the old "mutationism" and bear no resemblance at all to the views based on experiment currently held by British and American (and other) biologists for over thirty years. Until the significance of Fisher's demonstration of the efficacy and paramount importance of selection, and of the minimal immediate evolutionary consequences of mutation is realized (so well stressed by E. Mayr), and until it is realized that if mutation were to stop today there is sufficient potential variance in wild populations, because of mutants already accumulated, to ensure that lack of new mutations would be no limiting factor on further evolution for immeasurable time to come, it is to be feared that misunderstandings in this very central field will not be resolved.

Now that the significance of the recessive condition of characters controlled by genes has been recognized, attention may be turned to a little *pons asinorum* which laymen have to cross if they want to understand how genetics provides the mechanism required to explain evolution by natural selection. The majority of genes become recessive, under the conditions that prevailed when they mutated, if they are deleterious; how, then, can genes be appealed to in order to provide the material of favourable variation on which evolution by natural selection depends? The first point to recognize here is that species in nature are crammed full of recessive genes, as S. S. Tschetwerikoff showed. The recessive state is a sort of sanctuary in which genes that are not wanted at the moment can be kept without causing much trouble in a sort of "bank," ready for use when conditions change, and the effects which they produce, from having been deleterious, may then become advantageous. Of this there are now several experimental demonstrations, of which it will be sufficient to mention the phenomenon of industrial melanism, elucidated by H. B. D. Kettlewell; sickle trait and the immunity to malaria which it conveys, studied by A. C. Allison; and banding in snails, studied by A. J. Cain and P. M. Sheppard. Many of these cases, in which it can be shown that the heterozygote is favoured by selection, lead on to the very fruitful study of polymorphism, predicted by Fisher and demonstrated by Ford, with great success in Batesian mimicry as C. A. Clarke and P. M. Sheppard showed.

There is a further feature of genetics that is worthy of mention. It is selection, not mutation, that determines the course, direction, and speed of evolution. Selection is able to do this as a direct consequence of the Mendelian mechanism, which is capable of producing great stability in some circumstances and great diversity in others. It is able to do this because genes mutate seldom, are never contaminated, and co-adapted genes can be kept together by the evolution of supergenes, which accounts for stability. But they do mutate, are recombined, and can cross over between their chromosomes, which accounts for diversity. Which of these two mechanisms prevails depends on the environment and the conditions of selection. As an evolutionary mechanism, genetics is extraordinarily supple and is, itself, an adaptation that has had immeasurable consequences.

Among the numerous contributions to genetics made by T. Dobzhansky, there is one which finds a most appropriate place here, for it concerns the intimate integration of genetical and cytological aspects of research and also demonstrates the importance of the part played by selection in nature. It concerns the inversions of "long" chromosomes, widespread among organisms in general, and studied by him in different species of *Drosophila*. By following the patterns of these inversions in flies taken from different localities, he has not only been able to demonstrate the derivation of one species from another—in other words, to construct phylogenetic charts on the basis of gene rearrangements—but also to show how the different gene rearrangements are adjusted to the ecological conditions which change with the seasons. The result is that the proportions in which the different gene rearrangements are found in the populations alter, and the speed at which they do this can be explained only by natural selection.

It was inevitable that the characters whose modes of inheritance were first studied were those that could be distinguished qualitatively. It was soon discovered that other characters were dependent on the operation of several genes producing similar and additive effects, as was demonstrated by H. Nilsson-Ehle and E. M. East. These multiple factors behave like other genes as regards segregation and recombination but, as K. Mather showed, they require special statistical techniques for their study. Characters controlled in this way include size, weight, pigmentation, and, in man, mental capacity, defects in which have been fruitful objects of study by L. S. Penrose.

Although artificial selection of cultivated plants and domestic animals, largely bearing on multiple genes, has been practised by man since neolithic times, it was only in the eighteenth century that planned selection came in, as a result of which Louis de Vilmorin raised the sugar content of beets by 20 per cent. Application of genetic principles has resulted in great improvements in yield and in adaptation to different climates in maize, for example, but less progress has been made in improvement of livestock.

When a brief and necessarily incomplete sketch of the history of a whole branch of science is under review, it is proper to assess its place in the body of science since its inception, in this case one hundred years ago. Like physiology, of which in some ways it may be considered a part, genetics is a meeting place at the centre of science, by reason of the multiplicity of its connexions with so many other branche of science.

Mendel himself introduced mathematics and probability theory into biology, where, at the hands particularly of Fisher, Sewall Wright, J. B. S. Haldane, and K. Mather, they have continued to throw light. From the start, genetics was intimately connected with botany and zoology, and later with cytology. Even palaeontology cannot avoid contact with genetics, for C. Diver showed that some mutants in the garden snail date from Pleistocene times, with interesting differences in the proportions in which they occur. In 1922, H. J. Muller drew attention to the analogy between the gene and the bacteriophage which had then recently been discovered by F. W. Twort and F. d'Hérelle, and, from J. Lederberg's work, Mendelian genetics is now known to apply also to bacteria and to viruses, with fascinating new demonstrations of mechanisms of transmission by transformation and transduction.

With medicine, genetics was connected from an early stage, both in respect of inherited resistance to infection and of inborn errors of metabolism. It has now revealed the cause of mongolism (a supernumerary chromosome discovered by R. Turpin, J. Lejeune, and M. Gautier). The connexion between genetics and psychology is further shown by the hereditary nature of markedly high intellectual capacity, pointed out by Francis Galton, and evident in the families of Darwin, Huxley, Cassini de Thury, and Bernouilli, for instance, and of markedly low intellectual capacity as in the Jakes family, not one of whom was ever able to learn a trade. E. Hanhart has shown that there may be an hereditary component in forms of schizophrenia.

The recognition that the human blood groups are differentially correlated with diseases such as bronchopneumonia, toxaemia of pregnancy, gastric and duodenal ulcers, and, generally, with fertility and longevity, illustrates another connexion of importance. It may also be noticed that the differences in proportions of individuals belonging to the various blood groups in different races of man, exhaustively studied by A. E. Mourant, have enabled anthropology to estimate the affinities between races on an objective basis. It is also possible, as C. D. Darlington has shown, that phonetics, meaning the preferences shown by different peoples for particular pronunciations of sounds, may rest on a genetic basis. From their work on transplantation immunity, P. B. Medawar and his colleagues have shown that cellular genetics has a connexion with problems of immunology.

In its original form, as propounded by Mendel, genetics is concerned with only two cell generations: the gametocytes which produce the gametes and the random fertilization of the latter to produce zygotes. But there are fifty cell generations in the life of a mammal, and it is during the earlier of these that the genes produce their effects. Genetic characters are the result of developmental processes. This connexion between genetics and embryology, which thereby acquires an accrued importance, is a very fertile field which H. Grüneberg has opened up and called developmental genetics, while C. H. Waddington has approached it from another angle and established the concept of epigenetics. A simple example of research in this field is that carried out by Grüneberg and me on the dwarf condition in mice which is controlled by a recessive gene. It was known that eosinophil cells in the anterior lobe of the pituitary secrete a growth-promoting principle. Dwarf mice can be diagnosed shortly after birth by their reduced growth-rates, and examination of their pituitaries showed that they contained no eosinophil cells at all. It is therefore clear that the gene responsible for this condition produces its effect by depriving the mice of the source of secretion of the growth-promoting principle in the pituitary from the start.

No account of this subject would be complete without mention of the pioneer experiments in this field carried out by R. Goldschmidt and by Julian Huxley and E. B. Ford, which showed that one of the modes by which genes exert their effects is by controlling the speeds of chemical reactions concerned in the production of visible characters. In plants, W. J. C. Lawrence and his colleagues showed that the genes that control colour do so by regulating definite chemical processes such as the attachment of methyl, hydroxyl, or carbohydrate groups to compounds such as anthocyanin.

From such beginnings the analysis has been carried further in biochemical genetics, especially by the experiments of G. W. Beadle and E. L. Tatum on the genetic control of enzyme systems essential for the synthesis of different amino acids. This connects again with embryology, for it must be by means of enzyme systems that chemodifferentiation in early stages of embryonic development takes place. No less important are the researches of D. Lewis and his colleagues on the especially discriminating enzymes in plants that distinguish between standard and non-standard amino acids and, by not synthesizing the latter, make it possible for a plant to protect itself from its own toxic amino acids.

Meanwhile the chemists had not been idle. Research was carried out in 1871 by F. Miescher on the composition of the nucleus, which was obviously connected with heredity, because paternal factors are conveyed by the sperm, and the sperm head is practically nothing but nucleus. In 1889 Richard Altmann made purified preparations of nucleic acid, to which he gave its name. It turned out to be composed of phosphate, sugar, and nucleotide bases, purines and pyrimidines, which the organic chemists patiently identified by means of spade-work which was to lead to the discovery of the composition and structure of DNA. By 1948, it was known that the DNA-content of diploid nuclei was constant from one tissue to another of the same species, except for the germ-cells, which of course are haploid and contain only half the quantity of DNA. It was also known that the four nucleotide bases are not present in equal amounts, that there is stoichiometric equality between the sum of purines and the sum of pyrimidines, and that there is equivalence of quantity of adenine plus thymine, and of guanine plus cytosine.

There still remained, however, a vast amount of knowledge to be gained before the chemical structure of both types of nucleic acid, now known as DNA and RNA, could be elucidated. It was not even known for certain that they were macromolecules. This advance was made by Lord Todd and D. M. Brown who, by 1951, established in every detail, including stereochemical, the structure of the nucleosides and nucleotides and showed how they were linked together in nucleic acids, and that these were linear macromolecules in which nucleosides are joined together by phosphate links in the 3 and 5 positions of sugar residues. Next, Erwin Chargaff showed from analyses of DNA that of the four (only four) nucleosides present, the number of adenine (purine) molecules was equal to that of thymine (pyrimidine) molecules, and that of guanine (purine) molecules equal to that of cytosine (pyrimidine) molecules. Without this painstaking work by the organic chemists, further progress would have been impossible.

Physics then entered on the scene, and, by means of the X-ray diffraction method used in crystallography which M. H. F. Wilkins applied to DNA, he showed that DNA molecules from all sources have a constant pattern, and he calculated their approximate dimensions. With these and the chemical data, J. D. Watson and F. H. C. Crick in 1953 hit upon the idea of how the constituents of DNA were arranged in the molecule, and constructed their now world-famous model, with double helical polynucleotide chains joined by hydrogen bonds between the bases. This has given a picture of the physical basis of heredity, the mechanism of replication and of mutation, the genetic code of information by means of which inherited characters in offspring are linked to those of their parents, and the translation of this code into the first stages of epigenetics (embryonic development) from DNA in the nucleus to RNA in the cytoplasm, and the consequent synthesis of particular proteins.

As a result of the work of J. Monod and F. Jacob it appears that molecules of RNA act as "messengers" carrying the code of information from the nucleus to the microsomes or ribosomes in the cytoplasm of the cells, where chemical synthesis takes place. Here is another link with cytology. Furthermore, these workers, together with A. Lwoff, have revealed the existence in bacteria of genes whose functions regulate the activities of other genes, thereby providing an adaptive controlling system that works in response to environmental conditions, through the chemical interrelation of the enzymes produced by neighbouring genes. Geneticists and students of evolution will wait with eagerness to know if this is the mechanism whereby the phenotypic effects of a given gene in higher organisms are controlled by other genes of the gene complex, as has been seen in the work of Fisher and Ford.

If chemical synthesis is important in the life of a cell in an adult organism, it is even more strikingly significant in embryonic cells where the products of such synthesis are the starting points of differentiation in embryonic development. This is the significance of J. Brachet's discovery that those special regions in an embryo which, from their properties of inducing differentiation, are known as organizers are characterized by high concentrations of RNA. He showed, further, that in the embryonic organization there are gradients of RNA-content which agree with the axial gradients postulated and initially demonstrated long ago by C. M. Child. Here is another link with embryology. Yet another with both embryology and cytology was pointed out by A. Dalcq and J. Pasteels when they showed that, during cleavage of the egg, synthesis of DNA takes place in the nuclei during the period immediately following the telophase of the cell divisions and before any signs of the subsequent mitosis can be detected.

In embryonic development, genes do not all come into activity together; this means that some are repressed for a time. The repressers, as James Bonner has pointed out, are proteins, some of them histones, long molecules which appear to become wound round the helical spirals of DNA and inhibit them. The derepressing, or calling up into activity of genes, is caused by the activity of small molecules, and here hormones play a part, acting as switches that turn on genes in particular cells, thereby initiating the synthesis of certain enzymes, and starting cells off on a path of differentiation.

To these connexions between genetics and physics, chemistry, embryology, endocrinology, and cytology can now be added another, with carcinology. The base-pairing hypothesis led to the discovery of evidence of mutations in virus RNA by G. Schramm and H. Schuster, using nitrous acid. The same phenomenon was observed by A. Loveless, using alkylating agents, which had been employed for some years in cancer research, and the connexion between genetics and carcinology was further emphasized when P. Brookes and P. D. Lawley showed how alkylating agents such as mustard gas can bind together the two strands of DNA and affect cell division, mutation, and Ehrlich-ascites tumours of the mouse. A connexion between genetics and carcinology had, in fact, already been known since 1929, when C. Kosswig showed that the gene in the Mexican top-minnow, *Platypoecilus,* in which it produces black spots, if introduced by crossing into the gene complex of a related fish, the sword-tail *Xiphophorus,* produces fatal cancerous growths. A. E. Kehr has shown that genetic imbalance resulting from species crosses in *Nicotiana* produces tumours that may affect all the hybrids.

The work on alkylating agents also shows a connexion with the independent lines of research on mutagenic agents. After H. J. Muller had demonstrated the mutagenic effects of X-rays, and E. Altenburg those of ultra-violet light, C. Auerbach and J. M. Robson showed that mutation could be induced by chemical substances, to wit, mustard gas.

It is worth pointing out that, of every one of the many branches into which genetics has fanned out, not one is a dead end; all are ever-widening fertile fields for experiment and the acquisition of natural knowledge. One of them, ecological genetics, contains the master-key that has unlocked the secret safe of the process of evolution itself, through adaptation to environment, as was first proposed by Darwin and has now been confirmed experimentally by E. B. Ford and his colleagues. Geneticists may also take legitimate pride that their studies on allopolyploidy have shown a method by which new species can arise, even in the laboratory, as A. Müntzing and others have shown. It is perhaps insufficiently known that evolution is an experimental study. Evolution has produced what there is, which, in biology, means everything; and evolution will produce what there will be.

It is believed that Mendel hoped that his researches would supply what he, rightly, considered to be missing from Darwin's theories, namely, a mechanism of heredity and of the origin of heritable variation. This is exactly what Mendel succeeded in doing. It is said that, when he was disappointed at the total lack of interest which his researches evoked during his life, he comforted himself with the words, "The time will inevitably come when the validity of the laws which I discovered will be recognized [translated from the German]."

Evolution and Its Importance to Society

Essay commissioned by UNESCO, Department de l'Avancement des Sciences. From *Impact of Science on Society,* volume XVII, No. 1, 1967.

Introduction

While the evolution of organic beings is a biological phenomenon, for whose proper study a scientific training is essential, no effort has been spared in the pages which follow to explain the major principles and general concepts of evolution in simple terms for the benefit of the non-specialist reader.

It is biology which teaches us about the beginnings of the organization of societies, already discernible among animals long before the threshold of humanity is crossed, and it would be difficult to find a measure taken at the political level or advocated by philosophers or theologians, without biological repercussions on human populations. Unfortunately, some scientific explanations of the causation and regulation of biological evolution have been used as a basis for political theses, seeking unwarrantably to adduce biological justification for the application to human society of particular principles and policies which, incidentally, are widely divergent and even antagonistic, since they range from complete laissez-faire to the class struggle. It cannot, therefore, be stressed too strongly that the principles of biological evolution bear directly on biological processes alone, and only indirectly on sociological processes. Although the ordering of civilized human societies has restrained the action of certain biological processes, these have not, however, become completely inoperative, and society is bound to take them into account.

This introduction may be ended with a word about evolution and religion. Some people have thought that the two viewpoints were irreconcilable. In practice, all educated men are bound to accept evolution as a factual premise. Only a few systems of theology find it a stumbling block, and, frankly, the conflict—if conflict there be—is merely over a few points on which science cannot compromise.

Origins of the Concept of Evolution

While the natural sciences are international, major ideas usually originate from one focal point from which they radiate, and the concept of evolution, in its modern sense, is French in origin. The fixity theory maintained that living species were immutable. The evolutionary theory maintains, on the contrary, that they have undergone a series of transformations throughout geological time. Hence the use in French of the term *transformisme* to designate this theory, in some ways preferable to the term "evolution," for two reasons. First, "evolution" in the eighteenth and early nineteenth centuries meant the stages a living being goes through in the course of its individual development from the egg to the adult stage (ontogeny), bringing the possibility of confusion with the word's palaeontological meaning of development of species (phylogeny). The term "evolution" was used for the first time in its modern meaning by Etienne Geoffroy Saint-Hilaire in his *Mémoire sur les Sauriens de Caen,* published in 1831. In the following year, Charles Lyell used it in the same sense in the second volume of his *Principles of Geology,* published in 1832.

The second reason is that the term *transformisme* implies nothing about whether a phylogenetic series represents a progression or a retrogression, whereas "evolution" implies progression; in fact, among plants and animals alike, there is no lack of species which have become parasitic or otherwise degenerate, and whose organization exhibits retrogression in relation to that of their ancestors, but which have still "evolved." Be that as it may, it is the term "evolution" which has won acceptance in this sense.

It is true that the ancient Greeks, and notably Empedocles, already entertained notions which might, at a pinch, be called evolutionary, but their ideas were based on philosophical speculation rather than on the objective study of nature. Nearer the present day, it was the discovery in Java of small gliding mammals, the Galeopitheci, then thought to be bat-winged monkeys, which suggested to Montesquieu the possibility of a progression from bat to monkey via *Galeopithecus*. "This," he said in 1721, "would seem to corroborate my feeling that the differences between animal species can daily increase and similarly decrease; in the beginning there were very few species, and they have multiplied since." Starting from 1751, Maupertuis, reasoning from the birth of monsters and the transmission of hereditary traits, conceived the possibility of explaining the multiplication of species as the result of fortuitous recombinations of the elementary particles of a living being, leading to the formation of offspring deviating from the ancestral form, so that "repeated deviations resulted in the infinite variety of animals that we see today, which may increase further as time goes on, but to which the passage of the ages will perhaps add only imperceptibly." Here are not only the concept of *transformisme* but an attempt at explanation.

This idea was revived and developed by Diderot in 1753: "when we consider the animal kingdom and remark that, among the quadrupeds, there is not one whose physical functions and parts, particularly internal, are not entirely similar to those of any other, might we not readily believe that there was never more than one primal animal, which was the prototype of all animals, with nature merely lengthening, shortening, transforming, multiplying or obliterating certain of its organs?" At about the same time, Buffon published his monumental work, in which, in the chapter on the ass, he raises the possibility of its being related to the horse, and speculates on whether these two animals are of the same family and have a common ancestry. But he recoils from the logical inferences of his thinking: "If once we agree that the ass belongs to the horse family and differs from the horse only because it has degenerated, it can equally well be claimed that the ape belongs to the human family, that it is a degenerate man, and that man and ape have a common origin." This would have been a dangerous departure from orthodoxy, and to orthodoxy Buffon surrendered.

Evolution was next propounded by Erasmus Darwin, physician, poet and philosopher, and grandfather of Charles Darwin. In a book on which he worked from 1771 to 1794, he concluded that evolution was true, on the strength of the changes undergone by animals in the course of their embryonic development (transformation of the chrysalis into a butterfly, or of the tadpole into a frog), of the transformations observed in cultivated plants and domestic animals as a result of selective breeding by man since the Neolithic Age, of the changes resulting from crossing, of the significance of vestigial organs and monstrous births, and of the vertebrates' mutual structural resemblances. As an explanation of evolution he suggested that the efforts elicited from animals by their desires and aversions, pleasures and pains, and the satisfaction of their needs, would have brought about morphological changes, which were transmitted to their descendants. His book was placed on the Index.

Independently of Erasmus Darwin, a very similar view was reached by Jean Baptiste de Monet de Lamarck in 1809. Assigned the task of classifying the very rich collections of plants and animals of the Muséum National d'Histoire Naturelle, he had so much difficulty in demarcating species and varieties that he concluded that in principle no such demarcations existed, and that species could be linked in finely graded series, provided that enough of them were studied and that they were sufficiently akin. In actual fact, this proposition is not tenable, because differences between species do exist, however slight and difficult to spot they may be. However, Lamarck contrived to construct a system in the form of a genealogical tree, beginning with the microscopic organisms and ending with man himself, with branchings indicating the common origins of diverse groups of animals. It is to this system, which had the merit of presenting the first tabulation of biological evolution, that the term "Lamarckism" should be applied. Unfortunately, Lamarckism has acquired quite another meaning as a result of Lamarck's attempt to explain evolution in the light of two principles. First of all he postulated, but provided no evidence for, a trend to improvement which he conceived of as having impelled the animals to mount the ladder of life towards man. Next, like Diderot and Erasmus Darwin, but innocent of the slightest suggestion of plagiarism, he postulated an "inner feeling," prompting animals to make movements, to form habits, and to experience needs, and consequently to develop organs to satisfy them. Therefore, like all his predecessors, he relied on the supposed heritability of the characters acquired by individuals during their lifetime, to conserve for their offspring the modifying effects exerted by environment on the form and organization of living beings. It is to this hypothesis and to the hypothesis of the direct influence of environmental factors on the behaviour and form of animals that the term "Lamarckism" is applied today—improperly and unfairly, because Lamarck is not the originator of the hypothesis (which, anyway, is obsolete) of the inheritance of acquired characters, and he did not claim a direct effect of environmental factors on the organism.

The notion of the inheritance of acquired characters, the falseness of which was not proved until the twentieth century, belongs to the old stock of human beliefs—but is none the sounder for that. It is found among the Hebrews, in the story of Jacob and Laban, who agreed that if any spotted and speckled kids were born in Laban's flocks, they would belong to Jacob, and the others to his master Laban. Jacob so contrived that, in the act of mating, the best goats—which means that he selected them—had "speckled and spotted" green and white rods before their eyes. This application of the principle of maternal impressionability resulted in the birth of sturdy "ringstraked, speckled, and spotted" kids for Jacob and feeble unspotted kids for Laban. On the strength of the very same belief, in Norway it was forbidden to display hares in food-shop windows, lest pregnant women, after seeing them, should give birth to harelipped children. In both cases it was assumed that the mother would transmit to her child, by the mechanisms of heredity, the effect of an impression she had received before its birth.

According to a legend in Greek mythology, Phaethon, the son of Apollo, was given permission by his father to drive the sun chariot through the sky, but such was his clumsiness that at one moment he came too near the earth, and the inhabitants of one region were burnt so deeply that their skins became black—hence the origin of the Negro races. Lastly, Ovid, in his *Metamorphoses,* tells the touching story of Pyramus and Thisbe, two lovers who arranged to meet secretly under a mulberry tree, the fruit of which had until then been white. Pyramus, believing that Thisbe had been devoured by a lioness, killed himself under the mulberry tree, as did Thisbe, when she arrived and found him dead. Their mingled blood soaked down to the roots of the mulberry tree, and since then all mulberry trees have borne fruit of a red colour, a character acquired and inherited from the blood of the lovers.

The hypothesis of the inheritance of acquired characters is based on a false syllogism, as Conway Zirkle showed. Major proposition: the environment produces changes in the organism during its lifetime, which is often true. Minor proposition: parents produce descendants similar to themselves, which is often, but not always, true. Conclusion: parents changed by their environment have descendants showing the same changes as their parents, without having lived under the same environmental conditions, which is untrue. In all the experiments carried out, whether on plants or on multicellular animals, to confirm this view, those results which have seemed to do so are due either to faulty genetic control of the material used or to trickery.

However, it was not for this reason that Lamarck did not succeed in winning acceptance for his evolutionary theory. He had to contend with the opinion of Cuvier, whose palaeontological researches lent no support to evolution, since they showed no intermediate forms between the known species, and in each successive geological bed in the Paris basin he found a fresh fauna at a higher level of organization already fully developed, which vanished as if wiped out at the top of the bed. Cuvier therefore supported the fixity of species and the theory of the separate and successive creation of species, the succession of creations being marked by a progressive advance in organization, since the fossils in the higher, and therefore more recent, beds were more highly organized than those in lower layers. Lamarck also had to face hostile criticism of his explanation of evolution, even from people who, like Etienne Geoffroy Saint-Hilaire, accepted evolution but not the hypothesis of Lamarck, whose work bogged down in quicksands. It must also be borne in mind that the concept of evolution, dear to Diderot, Erasmus Darwin and Lamarck, progressive radicals, was out of tune with public opinion which, after the Revolution, in France as in England, wanted a stable society and recoiled from ideas stigmatized as subversive.

It was not until Charles Darwin that a decisive advance was to be made.

Evolution as a Fact

Charles Darwin's work falls into two phases: first, proving that the evolution of organic beings is a fact; and secondly, discovering the principle explaining evolution. Without retracing the development of Darwin's thinking or the laborious edging forward of his ideas and demonstrations, it will suffice to consider briefly a dozen scientific disciplines which all lead to the same conclusion.

Morphology, or comparative anatomy, shows fundamental similarities in the structure of animals of the same group. In all mammals, the parts of the skeleton correspond bone for bone, and are easily recognizable, whatever the superficial differences. The bones of the arm, of the forearm, of the wrist, of the hand and of the fingers, have the same fundamental structure, whether in the paw of a dog, the wing of a bat, the flipper of a whale, or the arm of a man. This resemblance is explicable only if all mammals descend from a common ancestral form and have evolved differently to fit the kinds of life they lead, while still retaining the essential underlying structure which testifies to their affinity.

Embryology shows that related animals resemble each other much more in the embryonic than at the adult stage, and it needs a very expert eye to distinguish between the embryos of such unlike species as the lizard, the chicken, the rabbit, and man. These resemblances can be explained only by the existence of a common ancestral form.

Ethology, or the study of the behaviour of animals, also shows similarities between the instincts of separate species, e.g., the mating rituals of sticklebacks, nest-building among birds, comb-building and honey-making among bees.

Several species possess obsolete organs, functionless and reduced to the vestigial state, such as the degenerate wings of the flightless ratites and penguins, in contrast to the functional wings of the ancestral forms. The same phenomenon can be observed in the minute vestige, found in certain marsupials, of the egg-tooth, which the young of their oviparous ancestors 120 million years ago used to break out of their shells and hatch. Another example is man's vermiform appendix which corresponds to a part of the caecum of herbivores, a cul-de-sac formed by the intestines and an organ essential in these animals (and to the distant ancestors of man) for the digestion of grass and other vegetable matter by bacteria.

The resemblances also extend to the chemical characters of organisms. Insulin, an enzyme produced by the pancreas, is a protein whose chemical structure has been analyzed in detail. It is, generally speaking, identical in wide ranges of mammals, except for certain amino acids in certain specific positions in the molecule. Thus, where insulin from cattle has serine, insulin from sheep has glycine; where both these species have alanine and valine, the pig and the horse have threonine and isoleucine; finally, where the pig has serine, the horse has glycine.

The fundamental similarity of the insulin molecule in all these mammals is a result of their common ancestry. The muscles of vertebrates contain creatine phosphate, a chemical which plays a vital role in contraction. The invertebrates, on the other hand, generally have arginine phosphate instead. This difference ceases to seem merely arbitrary if we take into account the fact that the vertebrates are closely related to each other and distinct from the invertebrates, with the exception of the echinoderms—which have morphological and embryonic characters approximating them to the vertebrates, in particular the secretion of creatine phosphate.

Similar evidence is provided by serology. The immunological reactions of different animals, which are linked to the chemical characters of their blood, make it possible to measure the degree of affinity between species. Thus, a rabbit, after an injection of human blood, produces an antibody which, if then mixed with human blood, causes 100 per cent agglutination. Mixed with the blood of a gorilla, it gives 64 per cent agglutination, with the blood of an orang-outang 42 per cent, with the blood of a baboon 29 per cent, with the blood of a sheep 10 per cent, and with the blood of a horse 2 per cent. This quantified seriation provided by serology agrees with the systematic classification of mammals based on morphology and embryology, and reflects the degree of diversification in the course of the various mammals' evolution.

Systematics, too, provides evidence. The hierarchy of taxonomic categories—species, genera, families, orders, classes, phyla—shows that plants as well as animals form groups which all fit in turn into larger and larger groups: species into genera, genera into families, and so on. This classification makes sense only if it reflects the affinities between different groups of plants and animals and represents the march of evolution.

The special feature of parasitology is that every parasite is living evidence of derivation from a free-living ancestral form, unless it be accepted that parasites (mistletoe, tapeworms, bacteria) were created on or in the bodies of the hosts, for which they represent a loss of nutriment, a source of discomfort or pain and often a cause of mortal disease.

A common feature of the scientific disciplines just surveyed is that they present a series of intricate facts which would remain arbitrary and utterly inexplicable were it not for evolution. Nor could the geographical distribution of vegetable and animal species be explained without it, and it was certain questions which occurred to Darwin in this connexion which led him to conclude that only evolution was able to provide the answer. Why is a species living in a particular area replaced by a different but similar species in a neighbouring area? Why do all South American rodents exhibit the same plan of structure distinct from that of Old World rodents? Why do the fossils of the huge edentate glyptodonts so much resemble the present-day armadillos of South America? Why do inhabitants of the same continent in general resemble each other more than they resemble the inhabitants of other continents? While the disciplines mentioned above do not directly prove evolution, at least they show that without evolution the world of living beings is incomprehensible. And the order in nature, so firmly demonstrated by the phenomena of physics and chemistry, affords convincing support for the conclusion that the phenomena of life are not arbitrary and inexplicable, but also conform to a rule of nature, which rule is evolution.

But biology can do even better. Palaeontology provides evidence, drawn from the successive geological strata of the earth's crust and from the fossils in them, that, for the past 2,000 million years at least, plants and animals have undergone transformation which, despite gaps in the series due to the chanciness of the fossilization process, can be followed objectively. The links in the phylogenetic chains, marking the stages through which the many kinds of living beings have passed, have not yet all been found, but we already have more than adequate data to enable us to trace not only the major lines of evolution, but also the intricate details of the transformation process in several instances. Further, the application of techniques borrowed from nuclear physics for the absolute dating of the different geological strata has made it possible to measure the differing speeds of evolution in the different lines. Thus we know with certainty that 60 million years were enough to transform a mammal the size of a small dog 12 inches high into a horse, and that in this evolutionary line it took 2 million years to achieve a systematic differentiation amounting to a new species.

Palaeontology is backed up by genetics. We know that the genes which control heredity and the development of the characters of organisms are positioned longitudinally along elongated bodies called chromosomes, found in the cell nuclei of all living beings. In the genus *Drosophila* Dobzhansky found in one species a seriation of genes which can be expressed by the formula *ABCDEFGHI*. But in other species the seriation of the corresponding genes follows the formula *AEDCBFGHI*. The genes *BCDE* have been inverted, and it is obvious that this species descends from the former. But the phenomenon continues with a third species with the linear order *AEHGFBCDI*. Here, it is the genes *DCBFGH* of the second species which have been inverted.

Lastly, for the past hundred years an example of evolution has been directly observable by science while actually taking place. This is the phenomenon called industrial melanism, which has transformed moths of the species *Biston betularia* from their original greyish shade to black, following the blackening of the landscape in industrial regions. On this genetic and ecological phenomenon more will be said later because of the principles of general significance which it provides.

Thus, a dozen separate scientific disciplines all offer evidence in support of the truth of biological evolution, and no science offers evidence against it. In the present article it is not proposed to deal with the evolution of life on earth in the light of the chemical evolution of molecules. It is a field in which there have lately been astonishing discoveries, but they do not directly affect society.

The Mechanism of Evolution

From the fact that there has been evolution, science then goes on to tackle the question of how it occurred and what caused it. It is here that the principle of the natural selection of hereditary variations comes in, discovered by Darwin, and adopted, with such amendments of detail as have been necessitated by the progress of science over the last hundred years, by the world's outstanding biologists. The principle can be summarized in the following seven propositions.

1. In all living beings an excess production of germ-cells is observable on such a scale that the proportion of these cells that survive and reach the adult state is infinitesimal.
2. The number of individuals in the various species remains fairly constant through good years and bad.
3. There is therefore a high mortality rate.
4. The individuals of any given species are not all identical, but show all kinds of variations in their characters; hereditary variation is a fact.
5. Some of these variations will be better adapted than others to the environment and the ecological conditions in which the individuals of the species live; those which possess them will survive and reproduce in greater numbers, provide a majority of the parents of the following generation, and leave the largest number of descendants.
6. The genetic transmission of hereditary characters ensures resemblance between parents and offspring.
7. Consequently, successive generations will maintain and improve the characters—anatomical, physiological and ethological—which make their possessors better adapted to the ecological conditions. It is through this mechanism that the adaptation of organisms to their environment begins and improves. It functions like a sieve which nature fills with individuals, letting through the best adapted and rejecting the others.

This system has been called natural selection because it does not rely on any principle not found in nature and because it operates automatically. It then remains to elucidate the origin and mechanism of hereditary variations, and here Mendel's great discovery comes in, that the hereditary characters of organisms are controlled by particles, later to be called genes, arranged in linear order along the chromosomes. Genes go in pairs, each of the two parents contributing one gene in each pair. When the individual produces sexual cells for the purpose of reproduction, the two members of each pair of genes separate, so that no germ-cell, whether ovum or spermatozoon, contains more than one member of each pair of genes. On fertilization, brought about by the chance meeting and fusion of the sexual cells, or gametes, the genes pair off again at random. As the two genes may not be identical in every pair, as a result of a previous abrupt change of a chemical nature called mutation, and as the number of pairs of genes in an organism runs to thousands, it is obvious that, through the action of the fortuitous recombination of genes after their separation when the germ-cells were formed, the number of possible permutations is astronomical. Mendel himself pointed out that if two parents have seven pairs of genes, and the members of each pair are different, the number of possible re-combinations totals 16,384 (or 4^7), of which 2,187 (or 3^7) will have divergent genetic make-ups. This gives an idea of the potency of the Mendelian mechanism as a source of hereditary variations.

Intergene contamination never occurs, even if the two members of a pair are dissimilar, and in multiplying during cell division they repro-duce themselves with absolute fidelity, until there is a mutation, of fortuitous origin, which changes the gene and the characters of the organism that it determines. After a mutation, the mutant gene con-tinues to reproduce itself without variation until a new mutation occurs and modifies it again, which happens on the average once per half million genes in each generation.

Following the remarkable discoveries of J. D. Watson and F. H. C. Crick, progress in molecular biology has made it possible to observe that the cause of genetic mutation is often imperfect reproduction of the deoxyribonucleic acid (DNA) molecule, the chemical substance of which the genes are made, in consequence of a change in the exact order in which the molecule's components follow each other.

Sixty years ago it was thought that evolution could be explained by mutation alone, since mutation is the only source of hereditary variation, but the idea soon had to be abandoned for two reasons. First, the direction followed by a mutation and imparted to the character it determines is entirely unrelated to the ecological conditions in which it has taken place; in other words, mutations are not adaptive—they do not do "the necessary" to advantage the organism in which they occur. Hence it is impossible to explain the origin and progress of adaptation in terms of mutation. "Mutationism" was therefore aban-doned over forty years ago, though this fact does not seem to be appreciated as generally as it should be. The problem of the mechanism of evolution was solved, as a result of extensive experiments, in the following way.

Sir Ronald Fisher, who has contributed more than anyone else to the elaboration of the synthetic theory of evolution—a complete reconciliation of the hitherto conflicting points of view of the Darwinian selectionists and the Mendelian geneticists—showed that if a gene now evinces the quality described as "dominant" and causes the emergence of the character it controls while suppressing the character controlled by the other gene in the pair known as "recessive," the reason is that it has *become* dominant, little by little, from the development of a preliminary intermediate condition. This is what has happened long after the original mutation of the genes which, after a change in the ecological conditions, have proved to be such as to confer advantage on their possessors. There has been natural selection of these gene-complexes (i.e., the total combinations of genes) of the organisms, which enhance the effects of a favourable mutant gene, so that they appear in the characters which the gene controls, even if the mutation is inherited from one of the two parents only, which is the definition of "dominance." Conversely, in the case of mutant genes which inflict a handicap on their possessors—as is the case with the vast majority of all gene mutations—there has been natural selection of these gene complexes which reduce or even mask the effects of the mutant gene, so that they appear in the organism only if the mutant gene is inherited from both parents; this constitutes recessiveness. This again means that the recessive genes have *become* recessive and that, at the gene-complex level, natural selection succeeds in producing gradual changes, very different from the saltations and sudden changes postulated by the mutationists. Nor is this a mere hypothesis: it is an objective fact, for E. B. Ford has shown, under rigorous experimental conditions, that a mutant gene can become dominant in one strain and recessive in another, according as the experimenter breeds for a few generations from individuals selected for gene-complexes respectively enhancing or reducing, however slightly, the effects of the particular gene on the character it influences.

From these experiments there emerges a conclusion of capital importance—that it is selection and not mutation which directs the ultimate progress of hereditary variations. Mutation has no immediate effect on evolution; all that it does is to form a contingency reserve of new genes which, as S. S. Tschetwerikoff showed in 1926, are held in the recessive state until such time as changed environmental conditions (and they are always changing unpredictably in one way or another) are favourable for this or that gene to confer advantage on its possessor. From then on, that particular gene will become dominant and manifest its influence. Proof of this is provided by a number of controlled experiments, more particularly on sickle-cell anaemia in man, mimicry in butterflies, and "industrial melanism" in moths and spiders.

To take an example, up till 1850, the peppered moth was found in England in the grey variety known as *Biston betularia,* which was admirably adapted to blend in with the lichen of the trees on which the moth settles. After that date a mutation produced a dark, melanic variety known as *carbonaria,* highly visible on tree bark and lichen. This melanic hereditary variation is caused by a mutant gene, but moths with the gene were repeatedly eliminated because their very striking colour when they settled on trees betrayed them to birds. The *carbonaria* variety only persisted in the population, and even then at a minimum level, owing to the occurrence again and again of the same mutation, which incidentally is a proof of the blindness with which mutation operates. However, the Industrial Revolution produced a biologically unforeseeable change in the ecological conditions of the environment, and the pollution of the air by vast quantities of smoke and soot killed off the lichen and blackened the trunks and branches of trees in industrial regions. Under these new conditions, it was the *carbonaria* variety which was at an advantage, and the *betularia* form at a disadvantge. H. B. D. Kettlewell was able to demonstrate this by direct observation of birds actually eating moths, and by measuring the survival rates of the two forms in the two environments, natural and industrial. The survival rate of the *carbonaria* variety was 17 per cent lower than *betularia* in non-polluted areas, and 10 per cent higher in polluted areas where today it forms over 99 per cent of the peppered moth population, while the original *betularia* form has vanished. Here, then, is a mutation whose effect was initially unfavourable but which, as the result of an unforeseeable change in the environment, produced a successful adaptation by the process of natural selection. This is only a tiny link in the evolutionary chain, but one which has been forged in a mere 100 years—a fantastically short period of time in geological terms, and there is every reason to think that the same mechanism, over thousands of millions of years, provides a sufficient explanation of all biological evolution. At any rate, this example, like so many others, proves that evolution is an opportunistic phenomenon, in which selection is all-powerful and mutation has only a very minor place.

This conclusion has received indisputable confirmation from another quarter, as a result of George G. Simpson's researches in palaeontology. It is known that at the beginning of the Tertiary era, 60 million years ago, the ancestors of the horse were small mammals the size of a dog 12 inches high, with four-toed feet adapted to wet ground, and short teeth for masticating the soft foliage of shrubs. If we follow very closely the fossil sequence of this family of animals, we see that their evolution was anything but rectilinear, since we can make out three successive changes of line, each dictated by the ecological conditions under which the animals lived. During the first period, the marshy ground and prevailing vegetation favoured the multidigital short-toothed forms; during the second period, when the ground was harder, the enlargement of the central digit of each foot to form a hoof, with the gradual disappearance of the side digits, conferred an advantage. Lastly, in the third period, the vegetation had changed as a result of the gradual drying of the land, and the animals' principal food was grass. But grass contains silica, which is extremely hard and wears away the surface of the teeth while being masticated. In these circumstances the teeth would have been rapidly worn to nothing, leaving the animals unable to feed themselves within a brief period, had they not developed teeth which were longer and permanently growing.

Further, as the animals' size increased, the neck and muzzle lengthened, so that horses can now graze in a standing position. Here again, we see that it was selection which guided evolution—deviously—towards a succession of different adaptive targets. There was therefore no fulfilment of a design, no rectilinear progression or "orthogenesis." Strains which continued along a line of development invalidated by some ecological change died out, leaving no descendants. In the course of his admirable investigations, Simpson succeeded in measuring the time necessary for evolution to effect a transformation of the value of a transition from one species to another in the phylogeny of the horse; it is 2 million years.

Appreciation of the fact that mutations are blind, that they are of no immediate advantage to the organisms in which they occur, and that the vast majority are reduced to recessives by the operation of natural selection, has another consequence. A number of theories have sought to explain evolution on the postulate of mutation's being given a direction conferring advantage on the organism, whether by the inheritance of acquired characters, or by "inner feelings," environmental stimuli, fulfilment of a design or programme, orthogenesis, vital impulse, or anything else. The objection to all these theories is the fact that mutations are not advantageous in the conditions obtaining when they occur. Mutations are unfavourable to begin with because, in the situation prevailing when they happen, the organism is already fairly well adapted to its environment, and a random change is more likely to be harmful than helpful to it.

These conclusions make it possible to express an opinion on one of the burning questions of our time: the probable effects of an increase in radioactivity as a result of fall-out after atomic explosions or accidents. It is a proven fact that the normal frequency of mutation can be increased by chemical and physical agents, of which radiation is the most potent. What will be the effects of these accelerated mutations on evolution? We can expect an increase in the ill-effects—miscarriages, monsters and still-born children; and an increase in the number of adverse if not lethal mutations. However, as it is selection and not mutation which sets the course of evolution, E. B. Ford and other scientists conclude that while such mutations could lead to an increase in the death-rate, they would not thereby affect the direction of evolution, unless the mortality were so high that the species died out. The same conclusion may be drawn from Bruce Heezen's hypothesis that the periodic reversals of the earth's magnetic field in geological times—the magnetic field dropping to zero before rising in the opposite direction—permitted an increase in the intensity of cosmic ray bombardment of the earth, while it was thus deprived of the shield provided by the magnetic field. Such intensified bombardments by cosmic rays could lead to species' becoming extinct, but would not modify their evolution.

The synthetic theory of evolution has also thrown light on the manner in which evolution has taken place. It was not isolated pairs of individuals that produced the new forms, because strains descended from one couple only are necessarily inbred and hence incapable of varying, of adapting and of surviving changes in environmental conditions. It has been more a matter of entire populations participating in the process.

The real importance of the Mendelian genetic mechanism lies in the fact that the recombinations of genes at each fertilization offer an astronomical number of possible hereditary variations, and it is on these that natural selection works. Evolution can even be defined as a statistical change in the proportion of the different genes in a population, since genetically a population is on a "common market" footing, and the bulk of each generation consists of the offspring of those parents whose genes have most effectively secured the adaptation of individuals to their environment. It is calculated that Man's ancestors formed a population 125,000 strong a million years ago, when they were moving from the pre-hominid *Australopithecus* to the hominid *Pithecanthropus* stage.

The haphazard nature of mutation has led some people to assert that evolution cannot be the result of such accidents. But, be it repeated, it is not mutation which directs evolution but selection, which, far from being fortuitous, is strictly determined by the ecological conditions. As to evolution, we have already seen why it is opportunistic in character.

The Bioligical Basis of the Evolution of Man

The oldest known fossils are nearly 2,000 million years old. They are fossils of algae and unicellular fungi. The existence of these two types of life allows one conclusion to be drawn forthwith. Algae, which contain chlorophyll, are autotrophic and take nothing from other life-forms, as they are able to synthesize living matter—proteins, carbohydrates and fats, which are called organic compounds—from simple chemicals, described as inorganic and found all over the world, like water, carbonic acid gas, nitrates and phosphates, with the aid of solar energy. Fungi, on the other hand, contain no chlorophyll and do not carry out this synthesis, but use the waste products and decaying substance of other living beings; they are saprophytes, feeders on decay. This means that, even at this remote period, certain organisms had already discovered how to obtain the organic compounds needed for their nourishment without having to synthesize them.

Later on, organisms evolved which carried the technique of living on other living beings even further, by the simple process of killing and eating them; these are the members of the animal kingdom which, in the final count, are utterly dependent on the existence of the vegetable kingdom for continued life, since they have lost the power to synthesize organic chemical compounds.   Moreover, as these compounds are not to be found just anywhere, but only in the substance of plants or the bodies of other animals, animals have acquired and developed the power of movement and sense organs and nervous centres which help to direct their continual hunt for food.   As out-and-out heterotrophs, animals are all parasitic on plants or on other animals, which themselves are parasitic on plants in the food-chain.

There is another point to note concerning the first known fossils: they were unicellular, and unicellular creatures are potentially immortal, since they themselves can become the sexual cells from which successive generations will emerge, a destiny of which only accidents can deprive them.   But, as soon as we get properly into the multicellular stage of organization, with its improved possibilities of increases in size and specialization of different parts of the body to fit new functions— whether in plants or in animals—the body of the organism is necessarily doomed to die.   Only the sexual cells, being unicellular, are in principle immortal, since it is only accidents which deprive them of the possibility of forming an organism which will survive after the death of the parents.

As the evolutionary procession passes through the successive levels of the animal kingdom, parts of it stray in every direction, down blind alleys leading only to extinction, as palaeontology and the geological record show.   The number of animal species known today comes to roughly 1.5 million, and it is reckoned that this figure represents 1 per cent of all the animal species which have ever existed.   Of the lines which survived, those which interest us most are, naturally, the primitive mammals, which first appeared during the Triassic period 200 million years ago, but were able to radiate only after the extinction of the dinosaurs at the beginning of the Tertiary period, 60 million years ago. Among them were small non-specialized animals which were the ancestors of man.   Quadrupeds like all primitive mammals, they became arboreal animals rather like tree shrews.   Next they developed the habit of hugging the trunks of the trees with arms and legs like tarsiers, which had the effect of initiating a bodily posture characterized by the erectness of the trunk—a very important stage in Man's evolution. Then came the habit of hanging by the hands from branches and moving about in this way; this is brachiation, the reason for Man's broadened shoulders, flat shoulder-blades and extensive range of possible arm movements. However, Man's ancestors used their arms for locomotion only for a limited period: they came down onto the ground, whereas their cousins the great apes remained forest-dwelling brachiators. The vertical position of the trunk, and the adaptation to it of the arrangement of the internal organs, led to the adoption of the upright bipedal posture as far back as the australopithecines, 2 million years ago.

The change-over from the tree-dwelling life to life on the ground not only affected our ancestors' anatomical characters, but also and above all their behaviour. Small, without any natural offensive or defensive weapons, slow runners, using two limbs only for locomotion, and in competition with the big predators, the australopithecines owed their survival solely to three developments: the perfecting of the brain as an organ to control behaviour, the social organization of their populations, and the perfecting of the hand, now freed from locomotory functions, as an efficient manipulative organ.

To a very great extent, these advances are due to a biological principle called paedomorphosis. For a long time the study of evolution was impeded by Ernst Haeckel's "recapitulation" theory, which held that the young stages of descendants of an evolutionary line recapitulate the structure of ancestral adult forms. In fact they do nothing of the kind, and a critical study of the facts and arguments advanced in an attempt to adduce the seriation of fossils in support of this theory leads to the conclusion that the order of the geological strata would have to be reversed to make them fit. On the contrary, one of the most important conclusions issuing from the analysis of this problem, to which embryology as well as palaeontology contributed, was the importance of a phenomenon which is the exact reverse of recapitulation. It is the adult form of the descendant which may resemble an ancestral juvenile stage, a fact which is observable in all groups of animals which have "succeeded" in evolution, and especially in the case of Man. It is the youthful state of *Australopithecus* and of *Pithecanthropus* which has been preserved in the adult state of modern man, a paedomorph with the build of a youth.

Paedomorphosis has been a factor of capital importance in the evolution of Man because it takes the form of a slowing-down of embryonic and post-embryonic development. This slowing-down is manifested in a whole range of characters, setting Man apart from his closest relatives in the animal kingdom, the great apes. The ages at which teething, sexual maturity, cessation of growth, suturing of the bones, etc., take place in Man are all evidence of this developmental retardation. Nor is this all: as Adolf Portmann has shown, the new-born human is still in an "extra-uterine foetal" state, with a year to go before the baby will have attained the same level of anatomical and physiological development as the great apes at birth. In other words, the human baby is born prematurely, and the reason is that in the birth process it has an obstacle to negotiate—it has to pass through the bony ring of the mother's pelvis. Even so, it is already a tight squeeze for the brain and its protecting skull. If development continued within the womb, and the brain grew bigger, it would not pass through. As it is precisely the enlargement of the brain which has been the dominant element in the evolution of Man, his post-natal development is retarded in proportion to the enlargement. Another effect of paedomorphosis is the loss by modern man of the heavy bony brow ridges of his adult pithecanthropine ancestors. Even more important is the fact that Man's retarded development condemned him to an extended period of vulnerable infancy, in which the individual was incapable of supplying his own needs and depended for them on continued parental care. The result was the establishment of the family as a stable biological unit, essential for survival, and providing a nucleus for social organization. The temporal overlap between generations in the home during the babyhood and childhood of the young of Man had tremendous consequences in that it made humanization possible, as we shall see.

At the same time, at the pre-human stage, it was only the improvement of their nervous systems generally and their brains in particular which enabled the australopithecines to adapt themselves to the requirements of their way of life—avoiding attacks by their enemies, and keeping themselves supplied with game which they hunted collectively, i.e., as a social group. Here the improvement was entirely governed by the effects of the mechanism of natural selection on the development of the brain.

However, it was not solely the action of natural selection which determined the general evolution of Man. Sexual selection also had an important role, and was responsible for many of the points wherein Man diverges from the pattern of the other higher primates, particularly as regards the bodily distribution of fatty tissue and hair and, probably, the development of a melodious and articulate voice, made possible by the mobility of the tongue, by means of which the resonance of the buccal cavity can be changed at will. Through the mechanism of sexual selection, aesthetic considerations were included in the selective factors, which, in the course of time, were to transform a female ape into the Venus of Milo.

Regarding the importance of the social factor in Man's evolution, it is essential to bear in mind the fact—which Jean Jacques Rousseau wrongly denied—that not merely did primitive man have a social life, but that so had his ancestors before they even achieved the hominid stage. Generally speaking, those of the higher vertebrates which live in groups have a social organization based on a hierarchy, with a scale of privileges and priorities, a "pecking order" to which individual behaviour is subordinated and which ensures stability and order. Natural selection favours the development of this kind of organization, because it tends to increase longevity and reproductive power. We already find a well-marked social order among the great apes, living in groups which are smaller in the forest than in open country where the dangers are greater and the defensive possibilities less. This was the pattern of living followed by the australopithecines, and it is estimated that their groups were between one hundred and two hundred strong.

The Cultural Matrix—The Condition Precedent for Humanization

At a still undetermined stage in his evolution, the development of the human brain (through natural selection) gave Man a range of abilities which more than offset his inadequate physical equipment for offence and defence. Speech allowed him to formulate ideas and to exchange and store up his experience, which memory converted into tradition, thus forming a link between the past and the present. From that point, through the power of reasoning, Man was able to envisage deliberate aims. A proof of this is to be found in the typology of his chipped flint implements. But this expertness in concept and execution, acquired little by little, is altogether different from the evolutionary advances which went before, since it is not hereditary, but handed down in the form of instruction from one generation to another. Education in being human, or, in other words, civilization, is simply this "tradition" in the literal sense of "handing down," whereby knowledge has been passed on and built up, as an acquired character which, like all acquired characters, is never innate, never carried by the genes, never inherited, and has to be taught afresh to each generation.

Every higher animal needs education. Cats teach their kittens to hunt; geese alert their goslings against the dangers they may meet. This, with the inborn instincts, is generally sufficient in the case of animals with their short period of immaturity, to equip the young ones. But with Man, childhood is so long, and consciousness, reason, and will have so much progress to make, that an outfit of inherited instincts would be powerless as a survival kit to safeguard the children against the many dangers to which they will be exposed. In place of the instincts there is substituted training relying on the neurological plasticity of the taught and effected through psychological interchange between children and parents, whereby the children, guided by their parents, slowly acquire an explicit knowledge of the world around them. Instinct is pushed into the background and, as C. H. Waddington has pointed out, is replaced by a predisposition to accept authority, the child's only safeguard during its neurological and psychological growing-up.

This is not all. The differentiation of the layers of the brain cortex and of the nerve tracts connecting up the nerve centres, which are the seat of intelligence, seems to depend on a normal progress of the stimulative exchanges between the baby or child and its family circle of parents and other children. This is the phenomenon that P.-P. Grassé calls the "group effect." When these stimuli are absent, as in the case of "wild" children brought up by animals (e.g., wolf-children) or secluded children deprived of the normal stimuli, the child does not get educated in being human. That is why the painter Auguste Renoir was quite right in his assertion that children are made by their parents —but after they are born. Which is another way of saying that the new-born baby is not yet a human being; it is one only potentially, and will become one only if it receives a normal social conditioning within its family.

If it were possible to imagine a catastrophe which wiped out every adult and adolescent in the world, civilization, too, would be wiped out since it is not a matter of heredity but solely of education. Now the education-based mechanism, described by Sir Julian Huxley as psychosocial evolution, produces results much more quickly than biological evolution, which is based on the hereditary transmission of favourable genes by the process of natural selection. As a result, Man is experiencing a new mode of evolution, whose progress in every direction on the material and technical plane has accelerated to a speed which is now frightening, and, for that very reason, risks exposing mankind to the ill-effects of a disproportion between what his recently acquired power over the physical world makes it possible for Man to do and what it would be wise to do, in terms of the general interests of mankind, particularly as regards relations between man and man. It is here that ethics enters the picture—a domain into which science is loath to venture for lack of objective evidence on which conclusions could be based. This consideration did not, indeed, deter Plato, Hobbes, Rousseau or Marx from participating, but none of them was a man of science. However, before tackling this tricky subject, we must revert to the matter of Man's biological evolution, for he is still, and will always be, under the rule of natural selection.

Natural Selection in Civilized Man

Although Man has acquired a new psychosocial mode of evolution, he is not exempt from the exigencies of natural selection, even if certain of its effects have been attenuated in the civilizations of today. In Sparta and in the Germania described by Tacitus, new-born babies were subjected to physical tests which only the strongest survived, and if they had the misfortune to be deformed in any way, their fate was soon settled. Modern civilizations in welfare states, on the other hand, take every possible measure to avert the dangers presented by natural selection for the weaklings.

This protective action even leads sometimes to a reversal of biological priorities. In the natural state, and right up till the nineteenth century in the West, the power of the least intelligent to multiply was kept in check by their lack of ability to foresee and overcome the difficulties of life. This is no longer the case today since, as a result of social benefits of all kinds, the less intelligent have a higher reproductive rate than those in the upper intellectual brackets.

Nevertheless, natural selection still acts on civilized Man, who has to thank it for an advantage which is often not appreciated. We tend to think that he has got so far away from the natural state that he is a kind of physical degenerate, and would cut a sorry figure if he were to find himself back in the conditions of life of the Palaeolithic age.

He would undoubtedly have difficulty in adapting, but Palaeolithic Man, in his turn, would have many difficulties in an advanced modern society. The fact is that modern Man has learnt to live in towns—a hard lesson whose stages can be followed in the history of Ancient Egypt. Further, he has improved his immunological resources against disease. Viruses like measles can only have become pathogenic to Man when human beings began living in close groups, thereby creating conditions favourable for the spread of epidemics. Before that time they were too sparse on the ground to have to fear anything serious in that way. Originally the measles virus was probably pathogenic, like rinderpest, to "herd" animals or dogs, and it was Man's living in close proximity to his newly domesticated animals which enabled the virus to change hosts. But it is to genetic variation and natural selection, favouring the resistant, that Man owes his present degree of immunological protection. Infectious disease would sink Palaeolithic Man at once, if he were subjected to the conditions of modern urban life, and it is with this danger in mind that several colonial governments bar certain islands in the Pacific to Western visitors, lest they pass infection to the natives.

For that matter, the immunological battle is far from won. In some cases, illness is attributable to inequalities in physical heritage, with some individuals genetically susceptible to infection, whereas others resist it successfully. Sometimes, of course, the hereditary susceptibility passed on by a gene is physiological and not immunological in nature, and takes the form of an inherited metabolic defect, as when the individual lacks the requisite gene for synthesizing an enzyme it needs for the synthesis or destruction of some chemical introduced into or produced in the organism.

Also to be borne in mind is the fact that adaptation in Man is not perfect, either anatomically or physiologically. An example of Man's imperfect anatomical adaptation is his liability to abdominal hernia, an accident arising from the greater elongation of the muscles and ligaments of the abdominal connective tissue as a result of a man's trunk and legs forming a straight line when he is standing, as opposed to the right angle formed by the legs and trunk of his quadruped ancestors. Though Man and his immediate ancestors took to walking upright on the hind legs several million years ago, the time which has elapsed has not been enough for the attainment of perfect adaptation to this stance.

As an example of imperfect physiological adaptation we can take the rhesus factor. We know that the rhesus-positive factor controls the presence of an antigen in the red corpuscles which provokes the formation of an antibody when introduced into the blood stream of a rhesus-negative individual. The rhesus-positive character is dominant, and if a male rhesus-positive homozygote (i.e., one who has inherited the gene from both his parents) marries a rhesus-negative woman, their child will be rhesus-positive. The antigens of the foetus can then pass through the placental barrier, enter the mother's blood stream and provoke the formation of antibodies which, in turn, can pass back through the placental barrier and may cause lesions and haemolysis in the foetus, fatal in an appreciable proportion of cases. This is an example of imperfection in immunological adaptation to viviparous reproduction. Yet, for 200 million years, mammals—including Man's ancestors—have been viviparous. Natural selection has not yet corrected this situation, which is due to the superimposition in Europe of a wholly rhesus-positive Indo-European population (among whom no such accident was to be feared) on another population which was wholly rhesus-negative (and, likewise, until then immune from such mishaps). These were the Ligurians and the Basques who still have the highest proportion of rhesus-negative individuals in the world. It was the arrival of the Indo-European warriors and their interbreeding with the Mediterranean Neolithic population they conquered at the beginning of the Bronze Age which produced the phenomenon, but natural selection is working to reduce its incidence, since every fatality due to the rhesus factor means the loss of a rhesus-negative gene from the population, so that the number of rhesus-negative subjects is decreasing. It is worth noting, incidentally, that if adaptation were "perfect," no improvement would be possible in a given environment, and evolution would cease until the environmental conditions changed.

Another most instructive example of the action of natural selection and of the part that it can still play in Man's evolution is provided by the "sickle-cell" phenomenon studied by A. C. Allison. Here a recessive gene causes the synthesis of an abnormal haemoglobin, S-haemoglobin, whose molecules tend to link up in such a way that the red corpuscle is no longer discoid but takes on an elongated sickle shape. From the biochemical angle, the difference between normal haemoglobin and S-haemoglobin is very small, consisting simply in the replacement of one amino acid, glutamic acid in normal haemoglobin, by another, valine, in S-haemoglobin. The physiological difference, on the other hand, is serious, because heterozygous S-haemoglobin individuals (i.e., those who have inherited the gene from only one parent) develop oxygen deficiencies in the tissues following heavy physical exertion or reduction of atmospheric pressure at high altitude, which produces haemolysis. With homozygotes, who have inherited the gene from both parents, the situation is even more serious, since they are doomed to anaemia, thrombosis and death.

By a fortunate but unforeseeable chance, S-haemoglobin prevents the malarial parasite, *Plasmodium falciparum,* from penetrating the red corpuscles and completing its life cycle there, so that individuals with this haemoglobin are immune to the disease. Thus a stable equilibrium develops, in the proportions of individuals in a population, between those with normal haemoglobin liable to die of malaria, those with S-haemoglobin inherited from both parents and likely to die of thrombosis, and those with S-haemoglobin inherited from one parent, enjoying both immunity from malaria and a chance of avoiding thrombosis, provided that their tissues' oxygen requirements are not increased too much.

In West Africa, a traditional endemic malaria region, the gene controlling the formation of S-haemoglobin occurs in 20 per cent of the population. The advantages enjoyed by the heterozygotes cannot prevent the persistence of an appreciable proportion of individuals who are homozygotes in respect of this gene, through the random mechanism of the process of Mendelian gene-segregation and recombination at each fertilization, though 80 per cent of S-homozygous children die before the age of ten. In the United States, on the other hand, where there is no endemic malaria and the S-haemoglobin gene confers no advantage, the descendants of the Negroes from West Africa comprise only 9 per cent of S-gene individuals. This reduction has been achieved in the space of about 200 years.

This example is instructive in several respects. First, it shows how an unfavourable recessive gene can, as a result of unforeseeable ecological conditions (malaria), become an advantage for its carriers and conduce to the survival of a certain proportion of them. Secondly, it provides an example of a statistical alteration in the percentage distribution of types of genes carried in a population over a known period of time, which gives us another definition of evolution, in terms of change and replacement of the genes in a population.

Lastly, we come to a question of keen interest to biologists and sociologists—the birth-rate. Among the higher vertebrates, the number of eggs laid by birds or young produced by mammals is controlled by natural selection, according to the amount of food accessible to the parents in their "territory" for feeding their young. We know that this question of "territories," or foraging areas, plays a very important part in the behaviour of the higher animals, while all fiercely defend their individual areas, especially during the breeding season and precisely for this reason. D. Lack has shown that the number of eggs laid by birds by no means corresponds to the number physiologically possible, and that for the highest survival rate we must look not to those parents which lay the most eggs but do not succeed in raising all their chicks, or to those which lay the fewest and do not hatch enough chicks, but to those which lay somewhere near the optimum number to make the living conditions optimal for their broods.

Man is the only species of higher animal to have broken free of ecological control of the birth-rate, which is what Malthus was driving at. In the Palaeolithic age, living a hand-to-mouth existence on the precarious and problematical results of their hunting and food gathering, men were constrained to practise and maintain the system of birth-control inherited from their pre-human ancestors, with some easing off, probably, in proportion as the improvement of their flint, bone, and wooden tools and weapons increased the yield of their foraging efforts. In the Neolithic age, when the benefits of agriculture and animal husbandry had banished worry about the very next day's food, populations started to grow, and within a brief space were being encouraged by the policies of the empires and great religions of the day. The Industrial Revolution, which began in the eighteenth century, stepped up the birth-rate even more. The world's human population, reckoned by E. S. Deevey to have been 125,000 a million years ago, when the australopithecines were giving place to the earliest pithecanthropine men, and 133 million at the beginning of the Christian era, had reached 1,600 million by the beginning of the twentieth century, is 3,000 million today, and will probably be 6,000 million by the year 2000. A physiological factor has contributed to this development. With woman's emancipation from the physiological condition of oestrus, which applied to the ancestors of the human race, as to other mammals, and restricted sexual activity to determined periods—which incidentally has permitted the establishment of monogamy—her sex life is not confined to spaced-out periods of limited length, and she can conceive at any moment outside actual pregnancy.

Be that as it may, the uncontrolled and anti-ecological multiplication of mankind is bound to bring catastrophes in the shape of famines, destitution, and population invasions, with natural selection brutally reasserting the laws of ecology, unless Man takes the necessary measures before it is too late.

Hereditary Variation and the Structure of Societies

A word remains to be said about the relation between the biological processes of hereditary variation and natural selection, on the one hand, and the structure of human societies on the other. The important thing for any species of living creature, including Man, is to be not simply adapted to the prevailing conditions of life, but adaptable to whatever conditions of life may develop in the future. The possibility of adapting is proportionate to the diversity and genetic disparity of a population, since it is these two factors which produce hereditary variation, the sole way, even if not 100 per cent effective, of avoiding the extinction of the species. It is here that the diverse modes of sexual union and marriage are important. In primitive communities the choice of partners follows rules made by the community to prevent both unions so endogamous as to approximate to incest, and wholly exogamous unions. This preserves the homogeneity of a group, in which the division of labour is based on differences of sex and age and on the "age-groups" studied by André Varagnac, who has shown that they already existed in the Neolithic Age and that some still persist, e.g., Boy Scouts, conscripts, and war veterans (perhaps we should add "Mods" and "Rockers").

Advanced modern societies exhibit a social stratification into classes between which unions, other than illegitimate, do not usually take place, which limits the possibilites of gene recombinations' drawing on the total genetic heritage of the community. Such stratification can have several causes, of which the earliest is the diversification of occupations. The land workers in modern nations are the descendants of the Neolithic cultivators, still profoundly attached to the soil. The craftsmen and technicians descend, primarily, from the smiths of the Bronze Age, reinforced by peasant recruits in the course of a long and gradual flight from the land. Then there are the traders and "clerks," and above all the warriors and priests, two groups which have played important roles in the social structuring of communities.

According to C. D. Darlington, it was probably force in the form of war, conquest and enslavement which did the most towards the establishment of social stratification in the communities of the past, resulting in a division of labour and distribution of occupations no longer based solely on sex and age but on racial mixtures. This implies a genetically heterogeneous community. In some civilizations, as in India, the stratification into classes or castes is strictly respected, on grounds which are religious, and the result is that the population does not get the benefit of the possibilities of genetic diversity. In other civilizations, the operation of the mechanisms of social elevation and degradation and of migration blurs the boundaries of the stratification and opens the different classes to continuous exchanges of members, thus increasing the genetic diversity of the community as a whole and, therewith, its ability to adapt.

In another respect, biological and psychosocial evolution in Man act on each other. It is through his genes that Man adapts to his environment, but he has already acquired sufficient mastery over nature to be able to adapt and choose his environment to suit his genes. There are no "cultural" genes, but there are genes which confer an aptitude for civilized life, and that style of life will last only as long as these genes are preserved. There is consequently a genetic and evolutionary element in the rise and fall of civilizations and empires.

Ethics—A Product of Evolution

Mankind is the only species with behaviour patterns calling on men to observe a specific line of conduct for the avoidance of unhappiness and the achievement of happiness, although the line itself varies with the theological and political ideals of the different civilizations that have held sway in space and time. To see this last point, it will suffice to compare ancient Sparta with the modern welfare state. We cannot but shudder at the thought of the religious or other intolerances which, in the past, and even, alas, in our own time, have given rise to regular massacres or expulsions, heavy with genetic consequences both for the nations losing, and for those acquiring, genes. But, given the fact that men in general have, and pride themselves on having, lines of conduct which they have agreed to call ethical, two problems arise.

The first is linked with the circumstance that, while Man is the only species in the animal kingdom to have an "ethic," he is also the only one to practise large-scale killing of his fellows—a rare phenomenon among the lower animals among whom, in any event, aggressiveness never reaches such a level. The reasons for this difference between animals and Man, so much to the latter's disadvantage, are still little understood. The researches on the ethology of animals being pursued by Konrad Lorenz and Niklaas Tinbergen may perhaps throw some light on this problem, and it is in fact possible that Lorenz may have found what is in principle the key to this paradoxical enigma. Among the mammalian species with bodily means of offence—claws, horns, hooves, tusks or fangs—which they use against individuals of other species, an inhibition has intervened in the behaviour patterns against the use of these natural weapons on individuals of the same species; it is an ethological intervention, starting from ritualism in conduct and favoured by natural selection, since it conduces to longevity and reproduction. Man, on the other hand, has no natural weapons and owes his survival while going through the pre-human stage solely to behaviour patterns which are not only aggressive but group-based. But Man is an extremely young species whose aggressiveness has been stimulated by the successive invention of the whole range of fighting equipment—from the flint axe via the bow, the sword and gunpowder to nuclear weapons—in the ridiculously short space of about 10,000 years, which is too short a time for him to have been able to rid himself of, or resist the impulsions of, his inherited behaviour, or of his proneness to be carried away and behave irrationally when he forms part of a crowd. This is a stage of evolution which has yet to be completed. It is against this background that the importance of the other problem set by mankind stands out—and it is of biological importance since it involves nothing less than the survival of the species.

The other problem is how ethics originated. In the nineteenth century, Thomas Henry Huxley pointed out that the ethics of men ran completely counter to the laws of biological evolution, a wholly amoral phenomenon. His grandson, Sir Julian Huxley, tried to solve this problem starting from the observed fact that there is a progressive evolution of ethical behaviour in societies throughout their history, and a progressive development of it in the child. What are the origins of altruism, devotion and compassion? The biologist notices that traces of these attitudes, however slight, are to be found even among the higher animals, in which the maternal instinct, and the instinct of the father to sacrifice himself for the other members of the family, are undeniable. At this level, the instincts are not conscious acts but inborn forms of behaviour subserving natural selection which favours strains possessing them. But once the pre-human becomes human, they could become conscious acts and provide at least a basis for ethics. Thus ethics, too, would seem to have been evolved, and that was the view Darwin was inclined to favour. For him, the great difficulty was the suffering so widespread in the animal kingdom. He conceded that, in Man, suffering might perhaps prepare the way for moral elevation, but remarked that the number of men in the world was nothing compared to the numbers of all the other sentient creatures, and these suffer, often appallingly, without hope of any moral elevation. He argued that it was comforting to interpose the laws of nature (hereditary variation; natural selection) between Creation and its Creator, whose direct handiwork it thereby ceased to be, and it was no longer amazing that a group of animals should have been created to lay their eggs in the guts and flesh of other animals, or that others should live on, and revel in, cruelty.

There are those who claim to see in evolution a manifestation of Providence, but this cuts both ways. First, it has to be recognized that hundreds of millions of species have been thrust into extinction, as the geological strata show us, and it is difficult to picture a divine Providence which produces or permits such slaughter. Further, we have the parasites and the predators, whose cruelty was so repugnant to Darwin.

Clearly if the march of events has not followed any guide line, the course of physical, chemical and biological evolution must be ascribed to the unpredictable action of blind chance. Darwin himself was conscious of the difficulty and declared that his metaphysical beliefs were in utter confusion. He found it difficult, he said, to believe that the universe was the result of blind chance, but study and analysis of its details showed him no evidence for a beneficent design or even for any design at all. Any conscientious and enlightened man of science is bound to come to the same conclusion.

Thus science is making it clearer and clearer *how* things happen on the physical and biological planes, but rigorously eschews any claims to be able to explain *why*. Perhaps it is wise to accept the fact that certain things are inherently incomprehensible to the human brain and to remain humbly uncertain where proofs are still lacking, pondering the words that Georges Duhamel puts into the mouth of his Professor Olivier Chalgrin: "To concede *ab initio* that reason will never explain everything is to give up before even starting and to open the way to fantasy, as I am well aware. But to assert that reason does make it possible to explain everything is to create a new superstition, to establish a new form of ignorance and barbarism [translated from the original French by UNESCO]."

CHAPTER

5

Embryology and the Evolution of Man

Essay invited for the *Robert Broom Commemorative Volume 1948*, pp. 181–190. Reproduced by permission of the Royal Society of South Africa.

The number of pieces on the chess-board of the problem of man's evolution is not very great. Including the general types represented by the Neanderthaloid, Java and Peking man and the Pithecanthropines, Taungs and the australopithecines, the living and fossil apes, old-world, new-world, and fossil monkeys, and Tarsius, there are only a few dozen pieces which students of man's ancestry push about the board. The way in which they arrange them is, of course, a consequence of the general principles of evolution from which they start, and it is therefore to these principles that I wish here to devote attention.

All workers on this subject would agree that their conclusions are based on "comparative anatomy," and would subscribe to the simple proposition that similarity of structure is indicative of community of descent to the degree that such similarity is detailed and extensive. This is the ground for including Homo sapiens among the Primates.

But there is scope for wide disagreement when the more detailed aspects of comparative anatomy are considered, and when questions arise whether one form can or cannot be recognized as ancestral to another, some authors are imbued with the value of the principle of irreversibility in evolution.

They hold that evolutionary trends, once established in phylogeny, commit the type to a particular morphogenetic policy from which there is no retreat. The effects of this view are negative and exclusive, in that they lead its protagonists to assert the impossibility of derivation of one type from another if the latter possesses a character which the former lacks. Possession of such a character, disqualifying the holder from participating in a pedigree, is called Specialization. The Neanderthaloid type possesses large brow ridges which modern man lacks; believers in irreversibility are therefore bound to exclude Neanderthal man from the ancestry of modern man.

Other authors are still caught in the coils of the theory of recapitulation. They hold that the young stages of ontogeny of a descendant represent past adult stages of ancestors in the evolutionary history. They are thereby led to the adoption of several far-reaching corollaries, such as the principles that evolutionary novelties can be incorporated only into a phylogenetic line at the adult stage, and that a character which appears early in the ontogeny of the descendant must have been evolved early in its phylogeny. This unfortunate theory, unsound in its premises, illogical in its deductions, and disastrous in its results, is now generally recognized as the impostor which it is. Perhaps the best demonstration of the absurdities to which the theory of recapitulation leads is that provided by W. K. Gregory when he wrote, "If the biogenetic law were universally valid it would seem legitimate to infer that the adult common ancestor of man and apes was a peculiar hermaphroditic animal, that it subsisted exclusively upon its mother's milk and that at an earlier phylogenetic period the adult ancestor was attached to its parent by an umbilical cord."

Nevertheless, the theory of recapitulation occasionally continues to direct opinion. One of the most curious things about it is the facility with which authors, even when forewarned, and by themselves, discard their critical judgement and fall into its trap. In 1929, F. Wood

Jones, to whom anthropologists owe so many observations of value, wrote concerning the theory of recapitulation that "its crudities are apparent to all biologists, its limitations are doubtless realized; yet when its teachings support any special thesis it is still invoked without hesitation or reserve." All the more surprising, therefore, is it to find the same author stating that "there is an order in the acquirement of ontogenetic characters, and specific characters, being mostly newly acquired characters, are determined late in ontogeny. We know that there are many factors that produce upsets in the sequence of ontogenetic development, but allowing for all these, it is impossible to avoid attaching importance to this fact of the merging of the facial portion of the premaxilla in the matrix of the maxilla in the human embryo at so early a period as the 24 mm. stage." The "importance" which Wood Jones attributes to this fact has been restated by him in the words "from its very precocious ontogenetic development it might be presumed to be a very early phylogenetic acquirement," and since the Taungs skull shows a facial suture between the maxilla and the premaxilla, he excludes the australopithecines altogether from the ancestry of man, which he places in the Tarsioids. All the similarities between man and apes would then have to be ascribed to parallel evolution.

A synthesis of modern knowledge of embryology, genetics, palaeontology, and phylogeny shows that there is no necessity for such conclusions which, in the case of the principles of both irreversibility and recapitulation, impose limitations on possible ancestry, which are in reality unwarranted.

It was W. Garstang who (in 1922) first showed that not only was the theory of recapitulation at variance with the facts, but that the direct opposite of recapitulation, viz., the evolution of descendants from the youthful condition of the ancestors, or paedomorphosis, must be accepted as having occurred.

These views were confirmed by me and generalized to show that Garstang's principle of paedomorphosis not only provided the most satisfactory basis for the evolutionary histories of some plants, many invertebrates, the whole groups of insects, vertebrates, ostriches, and man, but also that the chief characteristics of these types—their plasticity and capacity for further evolution—are associated with the paedomorphic mode of evolution.

Whether this association is one of cause and effect, it is as yet hard to say. From the point of view of genetics, evolutionary plasticity is the ability of the individuals of a species to show a high degree of variance on which natural selection can work, and this condition is fulfilled when the number of individuals carrying genes in the heterozygous state, and the number of such genes, are great. In such case, the possibilities of recombination of genes are wide, and there will be a reserve of recessive genes which may come into play as modifiers, in one direction or another, in the new conditions which recombinations and permutations of the gene-complex will provide.

It can be imagined that in a species undergoing paedomorphosis, there may be some genes whose functions included the control of characters which no longer appear when such characters are, as it were, dropped off from the end of the life-history. The gene-complex, however, remains, and some of its genes, partially "unemployed," may then exert controlling effects in new directions.

At the same time the association of paedomorphosis with increased power of evolution may be due to an effect to which J. Z. Young first drew attention. He showed that some environments in which organisms live must be considered as "difficult" and others as "easy." In general the environments in which adults live are more "difficult," specialized and restricted than the environments of larvae and young stages. It is possible, therefore, that the importance of paedomorphosis lies in the withdrawal of an organism from its "difficult" adult environment to the "easier" environment of its youthful condition, and that this opens up new ecological avenues of evolutionary possibility. Perhaps both principles are at work.

Evolution by specialization of the adult stages of successive ontogenesis, termed "gerontomorphosis" by me, is associated with the opposite effect of decreasing ability to evolve further.

Evolutionary novelties of recent phylogenetic occurrence can, and do, occur at early stages of ontogeny. Examples are the cases in which the young stages of closely allied species differ more than their adults: *Peripatus capensis* and *P. balfouri, Polygordius lacteus* and *P. appendiculatus, Acronycta tridens* and *A. psi, Rana tigrina* and *R. cancrivora* are examples (details of which, however, cannot be considered here) from widely separated groups of the animal kingdom. In one of each of these pairs a recent evolutionary novelty appears in early stages of ontogeny. There are also the cases in which dissimilarities between embryos and larvae of closely related or even identical species arise under different environmental conditions, to which A. Giard has given the name "poecilogony." Further, since it is now experimentally established that evolution can and does proceed by the selection of genes in a gene-complex, it is not out of place to note that a very recent mutation such as left-handedness in snails (e.g., *Limnoea*) can affect the very first cleavage division of the egg.

Lastly, even the egg and the processes of early development in the brown frog *Rana fusca* differ from those of the closely related edible frog *R. esculenta*.

The fact is that von Baer's first and second laws, that general characters appear in embryonic development before special characters, are not of general validity. A. N. Sewertzoff has drawn attention to many exceptions to these laws, of which it will suffice to mention the fact that in bony fishes a feature characteristic of the order (position of pelvic fins) develops earlier than a feature characteristic of the class (bony scales). To this I might add that "we are as old as our tongues and a little older than our teeth"; teeth are phylogenetically older than tongues, although ontogenetically they are formed later.

It follows, therefore, that the sequence of ontogenetic stages in the development of a descendant bears no necessary relation to the stages in the evolutionary history at which the characters in question were incorporated in the phylogeny.

The embryonic stages of the descendant do not represent the adult stages of the ancestor, but its embryonic stages. The gill pouches of the human embryo do not represent the gill slits of the adult fish ancestor, but the gill pouches of the embryonic fish ancestor. This is a simple matter of descriptive fact.

On the other hand, the adult stage of the descendant can sometimes resemble the youthful stage of its ancestors, the mode of evolution having taken the form of prolongation of the ontogeny and retention in the adult descendant of characters that were youthful in the ancestor. This is paedomorphosis. It was also shown by me that paedomorphosis allowed for the possibility that evolution, from the point of view of the palaeontologist, took place "clandestinely" in the young stages (which are soft and not preserved as fossils) of the individuals of phylogenetic line, the changes becoming revealed when the old adult stages were discarded. The sudden appearance of new types, and the apparent gaps in phylogenetic series, receive a logical explanation from the concept of clandestine evolution.

From the point of view of the origin and pedigree of man, the most important feature of the paedomorphic mode of evolution lies in the bearing which it has on the principles of irreversibility and of recapitulation. By the retardation of development, very marked in man, and the progressive retention of youthful ancestral characters into the adult stages of the descendants, the ancestral adult characters can become discarded. This is what is believed to have happened in the evolution of vertebrates from echinoderm-like larvae, the echinoderm-like adult form having been discarded; in the evolution of insects from myriapod-like larvae, the adult myriapod-like form having been discarded. The paedomorphic mode of evolution enables ancestral adult specializations to become discarded and lost. New trends of evolution can be superimposed on the old. If this is so, then there can be no justification in regarding the mere possession of brow ridges by adult Neanderthal man as disqualifying his stock from having given rise to the modern man. This view was put forward by L. H. D. Buxton and me in 1932; we based our argument not only on the biological importance of paedomorphosis in the animal kingdom in general, but also on the specific evidence for paedomorphosis in man brought forward by L. Bolk under the heading of foetalization.

Bolk showed that there was a marked resemblance between adult modern man and young apes in respect of: relative brain-weight, the brow ridges, the position of the foramen magnum, the degree of cranial flexure, the condition of the sutures of the bones of the skull, the eruption of the teeth, the flatness of the face, the hairlessness of the body, the light colour of the skin, and other features. An additional example has been supplied by Gregory. In young apes the frontal bones send down narrow processes which barely meet and therefore fail completely to separate the ethmoid from the sphenoid. In adult apes the frontals meet in the midline and separate the sphenoid from the ethmoid. Modern man resembles the young ape. In my *Atlas of Evolution* I have given other points in which modern man shows retardation as compared with other Primates, such as gestation-period, growth-period, life-span, onset of puberty, degree of ossification and amount of hair at birth.

By way of further illustration of the importance of paedomorphosis in incorporating in modern adult man characters which were embryonic or youthful in his ancestors, it may be of interest to give more examples of such characters. Devaux has drawn attention to the interesting idea that the moveable rosy lips of man can best be understood as an adaptation to prolonged suckling and must have originated in an infantile stage. They have been retained in adult life, beyond the period of their original usefulness as accessory feeding organs, and their present function of kissing may have been of considerable importance in the sexual selection which has undoubtedly accompanied the evolution of man.

Gregory has shown that a recently evolved human character such as the separation of the peroneus tertius from the parent muscle-mass originated in the foetal stage; conversely, he has shown that such a phylogenetically ancient character as the divergence of the great toe is not yet as much reduced in early foetal stages as it is in the adult. Similarly, some recently evolved characters, such as blond hair in Europeans, are less frequent in adult stages than in young stages.

These cases, which fall into line perfectly with the many examples given above from other branches of the animal kingdom, provide additional proof, if it were needed, that there is no inevitable correlation between the stage of ontogeny at which a character is developed and the stage in phylogeny at which it was evolved. It is in the light of these conclusions that the case of the obliteration in modern man of the premaxillo-maxillary suture must be considered. That this should happen very early in the ontogenetic development of modern man is no evidence that it occurred early in his phylogenetic history. A parallel case is provided by Sir Wilfrid Le Gros Clark, who has drawn attention to the fact that the assumption by the human foot of its characteristic form at a very early stage of ontogenetic development is no evidence that the human foot was evolved at a very early stage in human phylogeny. Indeed, as Dudley Morton has shown in his very careful studies of the evolution of the human foot, "the great ape or gorilloid type of foot presents an intermediate stage in structural and functional modification through which, *of necessity,* the evolutionary development of the human foot had to pass." If earliness of appearance of a character in man's ontogenetic development does not exclude the ape type from man's ancestry in the case of the foot, it cannot logically exclude the ape type from man's ancestry in the case of the premaxilla. Sauce for the goose may still be sauce for the gander.

Actually, the problem of the premaxilla in man has been solved by Ashley Montagu with the important observation that the period of development at which the suture between the maxilla and premaxilla is obliterated is correlated with the size of the premaxilla. This solution of the problem was predicted by M. Augier when he demonstrated the separate origin of the premaxilla in man. One of the commonest methods adopted in evolution for the reduction of structures is a decrease in their growth-rate. In many cases it has been possible to demonstrate that such reduction follows a negative equation of the allometric type, as was shown by Sir Julian Huxley. Such phenomena have no phylogenetic significance at all. Indeed, *complete* reduction of a structure resulting in its absence even in embryonic stages does not mean that the structure was not present in the adult in quite recent ancestors. The total disappearance of limb rudiments in snakes even in the earliest stages of development does not mean that the ancestors of snakes were limbless. And just as a vestigial limb can be interpreted only as the representative of a full-sized limb in the ancestor, so the vestigial premaxilla in man can be understood only if it is regarded as the representative of a full-sized ancestral premaxilla such as is possessed by the apes and may have been possessed by the Taungs skull.

The introduction of embryological considerations into the possibilities of what can and what cannot be deduced from comparative anatomy results, therefore, in freeing the field from the restrictive effects of the principles of irreversibility and of recapitulation.

There may be facts (such as the apparent relative chronology of the fossil finds if it be substantiated) which preclude the derivation of modern man from Neanderthaloid ancestors, but the presence in the adult of the latter of heavy brow ridges is not one of these facts, if the evolution of modern man took place from a Neanderthaloid stock by paedomorphosis and retention of youthful conditions with consequent discarding of some adult Neanderthaloid features. That an event such as this did, in fact, occur in the evolution of modern man is supported by the evidence presented by such young Neanderthaloid individuals as have been discovered. The Devil's Tower skull, the young Mount Carmel skull, the Usbekistan skull, the young La Quina skull all lacked the heavy brow ridges of adult Neanderthaloid types and present a condition from which adult modern man could without difficulty have been derived. At a lower level the same is true of the Modjokerto child's skull, which appears to represent the young condition of *Pithecanthropus*. It is interesting to note that the retardation in development shown by modern man as compared with the apes had not proceeded so far in the young Mount Carmel individual. Its dentition corresponds to the stage which in modern man is reached at the age of four to four and a half years, but is more advanced in its development than a modern child of a similar age.

The line of human evolution is believed to lead from prosimians with gerontomorphic twigs leading to the lemurs, tarsioids, monkeys and apes, until, after a crisis in the Miocene, paedomorphosis leads from the australopithecines through the pithecanthropines and the neanderthaloids to Homo sapiens; at the same time geronomorphosis has continued to claim a few isolated evolutionary victims such as *Paranthropus, Meganthropus,* the full-blown specialized Neanderthal type, etc.

The possibility that modern man was evolved from a Neanderthaloid stock was envisaged and accepted by A. Hrdlička from a totally different point of view. Starting from the facts that Neanderthal types disappeared suddenly without trace of successors, that modern man appeared suddenly from nowhere, that modern man took over Neanderthaloid culture, and that if modern man was not derived from neanderthaloids then it is necessary to postulate the existence of parallel lines of human evolution, Hrdlička concluded on the basis of economy of hypotheses that the evidence is most satisfactorily subsumed under the hypothesis that modern man was derived from a Neanderthaloid stock. As to how this came about, Hrdlička added the opinion that it took place by progressive infantilism, particularly of the brow ridges—an opinion with which I find myself in agreement. I. Kalin has also concluded that some hypothesis such as paedomorphosis is indispensable if modern man and the humanoid fossils are to be related phylogenetically.

There is a further principle of comparative anatomy of which little use has been made in the study of the evolution of man. It is the principle demonstrated by D. M. S. Watson in his studies on the evolution of reptiles from amphibia and illustrated by *Seymouria,* since then generalized by me (see page 140) under the name "mosaic evolution," to the effect that the transition from amphibian to reptilian characteristics does not take place by the transformation of all the characters here and there over the animal which, in the transition stage, is a sort of mosaic of characters, some amphibian and some reptilian. This is precisely the condition presented by the skulls of the Mount Carmel group, which T. D. McKown and A. Keith have shown to exhibit a mixture of Neanderthaloid and modern features, varying in each direction into the ranges of typical Neanderthaloid conditions at one end and typical modern human conditions on the other. An even better example is provided by the upright stance which australopithecines have been shown to possess, while their skulls were still ape-like. Since it would be an extravagant hypothesis to believe that the Mount Carmel people represent hybrids between neanderthaloids and modern men, implying as it would that modern man was evolved parallel with Neanderthaloid forms, and since modern man is known before the Riss-Wurm interglacial period, Keith has recently also expressed the view that the Mount Carmel forms are transitional between a Neanderthaloid type and modern man. F. Weidenreich considers that the Neanderthal type "has 'survived' by transmuting into *Homo sapiens.*" I should add that the method of "transmutation" was paedomorphosis. T. Dobzhansky prefers to believe that the Mount Carmel people were hybrids between modern man and neanderthaloids. But even on this view they become merely races of one and the same species.

If, as I believe, paedomorphosis was at work in the derivation of modern man from a Neanderthaloid stock, it probably also operated at even earlier stages of human evolution. The fact that the Taungs skull is juvenile, for only the first permanent molar was erupted, makes it only the more interesting. It, too, lacked the heavy brow ridges. Nor, even if it possessed a facial premaxillo-maxillary suture, is it on that score to be debarred from the line of human ancestry.

Indeed, it is difficult to disagree with Robert Broom's conclusion that "man arose from a Pliocene member of the Australopithecines, probably very near to *Australopithecus* itself." If the adult Australopithecinae (*Plesianthropus* and *Paranthropus*) were the only ones known, I wonder whether the closeness of the family to the line of man's ancestry would have been recognized. That it has been so is an implication of the value of paedomorphosis.

Nothing in the theory of paedomorphosis detracts from the importance of embryology in indicating affinities between groups of animals from the similarity of their larvae and embryos, as Darwin pointed out. The important point is that these embryos and larvae cannot be held to represent the adult ancestors. The most that can be said is that in some groups (e.g., vertebrates) the broad plan of structure is laid down in the embryo, and an inference concerning this plan in the ancestral adult can be drawn. In other groups however (e.g., insects), the larval structure reflects nothing ancestral at all, as Darwin well realized.

Evolution is not confined to modifications of the adults as Haeckel thought, but can start from modifications in young stages and, when it does, its results are the most striking. The variations on which natural selection may act are not restricted to the scale of variants represented by full-grown organisms, but also include variants along the time-scale of development, for all stages of the life-history are available for the selection of the forms most efficiently adapted to their environment. In all cases where paedomorphosis has occurred, there must have been an increased survival value for these variants which developed more slowly and did not repeat the final stages of development of their ancestors and brethren. Paedomorphosis must have conferred a selective advantage in each case, or it would not have taken place. What this increased survival value was in the case of the evolution of man is plain; for delay in development enabled him to develop a larger and more complex brain, and the prolongation of childhood under conditions of parental care and instruction consequent upon memory-stored and speech-communicated experience allowed him to benefit from a more efficient apprenticeship for his conditions of life.

I hope that it will not be concluded that the views here expressed have solved the problems of man's ancestry; all I claim is that a proper recognition of the part which paedomorphosis has played in evolution necessitates a restatement of the principles of comparative anatomy on which conclusions of possible or impossible descent are based. Such a restatement as I have outlined above removes a number of negative arguments and widens the possibilities of phylogenetic descent. In any given case these remain to be proved; it is important that they not be put out of court by erroneous and restrictive misconceptions before they are even considered.

CHAPTER
6

Mosaic Evolution

Presidential Address to the Zoology Section of the British
Association for the Advancement of Science, delivered on
September 2, 1954, at Oxford. From *The Advancement
of Science,* No. 42, September, 1954.

No man who has the honour to preside over the Zoological Section
of the British Association meeting in Oxford can be unmindful of two
facts. The first is the memorable meeting of 1860, when T. H. Huxley
championed Darwin's recently propounded theory of evolution by means
of natural selection, and blazed for it a trail which has now become
one of the greatest ornaments of intellectual endeavour. The other is
the fact that this meeting is being held in the Department which was
presided over for many fruitful years by that great master of zoology,
Edwin Stephen Goodrich. For half a century he devoted himself to
the study of comparative anatomy and embryology with the object of
providing evidence of the course which evolution has taken. Those
of us who had the privilege to know him have reason to be proud.

In searching for a subject on which to address you today, it is therefore not unfitting that I should select one bearing on the subject of
evolution.

I have a certain apprehension in speaking on any scientific subject,
particularly that of evolution, without having some solid object to talk
about so as to anchor my words to a firm sea-bed of evidence, and the
material which I have selected for this purpose is the specimen of the
fossil *Archaeopteryx lithographica* preserved in the British Museum
(Natural History), probably the most precious, the most beautiful, and
the most interesting fossil hitherto discovered in the world.

It is over ninety years since it was described by my predecessor, Sir
Richard Owen, and since then a few contributions have been made to our
knowledge of it; but when I came to examine it, and applied to it
modern methods of research such as photography under ultra-violet
illumination, I considered that it was worthy of a complete reinvestiga-
tion. It is some of the results of this work which I am putting forward
before you today for the first time, with the object not only of describing the new facts which have come to light, but also of providing
evidence on which I hope to demonstrate a principle of evolution which
deserves further attention.

Archaeopteryx and the Transition from Reptiles to Birds

The fossil is preserved in a slab and corresponding counter-slab of a
block of limestone from the Solnhofen deposit of the Jurassic, about
150 million years old. At the very first glance its most important
features become apparent, for while some of them are thoroughly
characteristic of reptiles, others are no less completely characteristic of
birds. It is this intermediate position which *Archaeopteryx* occupies
that makes it an object of such enormous interest.

First the reptilian features:

1. the long tail of twenty vertebrae, all of them free up to the tip as would
   be found in a reptile;
2. the simple articulation between the vertebrae without any of the com-
   plications found in birds;
3. the short sacrum, involving no more than six vertebrae by means of which
   the vertebral column is attached to the pelvic girdle;
4. the free metacarpal bones in the hand, and the presence of claws on all
   three fingers;
5. the free metatarsal bones in the foot;

6. the simple ribs and gastralia in the ventral body wall;
7. the simple brain with elongated, slender cerebral hemispheres, optic lobes, and a small cerebellum.

All these are characters which would not be in the least out of place if found in any reptile. On the other hand, there are a number of features in *Archaeopteryx* which are absolutely characteristic of birds:

1. First the feathers, the impressions of which show that they were composed of rachis and barbs forming the vanes, identical in structure with those in modern birds.
2. Next comes the fact that these feathers are arranged on the forearm to form a wing, in a manner again precisely similar to that which is found in modern birds. There is a group of flight-feathers called the primaries, inserted on the hand and wrist, and another group called the secondaries, inserted on the forearm; covering the bases of these flight-feathers are coverts.
3. Then there is the fact that the two collar-bones are joined to form a merrythought, a character found only in birds.
4. In the pelvic girdle the pubes are directed backwards, again as in other birds.
5. Lastly, the foot shows that the big toe was opposed to the other three toes, which is the characteristic adaptation by means of which birds perch on twigs of trees.

From the evidence already presented, it is clear that *Archaeopteryx* was an arboreal animal, and that it had the power of gliding through the air supported by the flight-feathers on its wings and those of its long tail.

For many years a search has been made for the sternum. The determination of this structure is of the greatest importance, since the absence or presence on the sternum of a keel is the evidence on which to conclude that the bird had weak or strong pectoral muscles, and either was not or was able to carry out vigorous and active flight. The sternum has now been revealed and shows no sign of any keel, so it must be concluded that *Archaeopteryx* glided rather than flew.

It may be of interest to show how the sternum was discovered. For this purpose it is necessary to look at a photograph of the counter-slab taken with ultra-violet illumination under which conditions bones are fluorescent while the matrix is not. Where with ordinary light there was little to be seen, under ultra-violet light it was at once clear that a hitherto unrecognized element was there in the form of a thin bony shell torn away from the main body of the bone on the main slab.

The corresponding place was then examined on the main slab. Between the left humerus and the left scapula a structure immediately became apparent and attracted attention. Having once been found, the structure was further revealed on the main slab by scratching away the matrix with fine chisels and needles. The sternum, for that is the only thing that it could be, was poorly ossified and must have been largely cartilaginous during life. Indeed, its spongy structure implies this. There remained to be supplied the proof that the structure in question is in fact bony, and this can fortunately be done by means of X-rays. There is a sufficient difference in density between the phosphate in the bones and the carbonates of the limestone matrix for it to be possible to reveal it by X-rays with suitable dosage, and the sternum throws its shadow just like the other bones of the skeleton.

Turning now to the brain: when photographed under ordinary light on the slab, it shows the natural cast as seen from the right side. The right cerebral hemisphere and the right optic lobe are beautifully revealed because the right frontal and parietal bones are detached and lie on the counter-slab. When photographed under ultra-violet light, the brain-cast is seen to be surrounded by a number of bones, among which can be identified the left frontal and parietal, the auditory capsule, and the occipital region. On the counter-slab the right frontal and parietal are beautifully preserved, and the hollow which they form fits perfectly over the shape of the right cerebral hemisphere and optic lobe on the main slab. Ultra-violet light confirms the bony nature of these structures.

The most interesting feature in the brain is the small size of the cerebellum, which did not as in modern birds encroach on the space occupied by the optic lobes. In this respect the recent investigations confirm the observations of T. Edinger (1926). There is an important correlation between the absence of a keel on the sternum, poor power of flight, and the small size of the cerebellum. It is the acrobatic power of flight of modern birds, made possible by the insertion of the powerful pectoral muscles on the keel of the sternum, that necessitates the development of a large cerebellum to co-ordinate the motor activities. None of this had yet happened at the level of evolution represented by *Archaeopteryx*.

Other anatomical details may be illustrated briefly. Among the new structures discovered on the counter-slab is a vertebra which for the first time reveals the concave and simple articular surface of the centrum.

Sir John Evans discovered in 1862 that *Archaeopteryx* possessed teeth on the premaxilla and maxilla. Ultra-violet light shows the details of these structures, and the way in which the teeth are fitted into their sockets and have a little pediment, like the base of a column. The presence of teeth in *Archaeopteryx* is, of course, not unique among birds, since the Cretaceous fossils *Hesperornis* and *Ichthyornis* possessed them.

Transition: Conversion or Mosaic?

From what has already been said, it is clear that *Archaeopteryx* provides a magnificent example of an animal intermediate between two classes, the reptiles and the birds, with each of which it shares a number of well-marked characters. It is, however, worth-while spending a little more time in considering what precisely is meant by the statement that an animal is intermediate between two classes.

If we look at almost any part of a living vertebrate animal, we can tell at once which class the animal belongs to: skin, skeleton, brain, heart, kidneys, are all stamped with the identity of their class. This shows that in the evolution of the classes of vertebrates as we know them alive today, all the parts of their bodies have undergone modification. This might suggest that in the evolutionary process which converted animals of one class into the next, there was a gradual and general transformation of the whole animal. If the evolution of the vertebrate classes involved processes of this nature, and an animal was caught in the transitional stage, the parts of such an animal would be intermediate in structure between the two classes.

On the other hand, the statement that an animal was intermediate might mean that it was a mixture and that the transition affected some parts of the animal and not others, with the result that some parts were similar to those of one type, other parts similar to the other type, and few or no parts intermediate in structure. In such a case the animal might be regarded as a mosaic in which the pieces could be replaced independently one by one, so that the transitional stages were a jumble of characters, some of them similar to those of the class from which the animal evolved, others similar to those of the class into which the animal was evolving.

If now it be asked which kind of transition is shown by *Archaeopteryx*, the answer is perfectly clear. It is a mosaic in which some characters are perfectly reptilian, and others no less perfectly avian. In its evolution from its reptilian ancestors, therefore, the modifications which it has undergone have affected some structures to produce their complete transformation, while other structures have not yet been affected at all. In the subsequent evolution from *Archaeopteryx* to the conditions found in modern birds, the latter structures, in their turn, have been affected, with the result that in the brain, vertebrae, sacrum, and carinated sternum, modern birds have got even further away from the condition of their original reptilian ancestors than was *Archaeopteryx*.

The condition in *Archaeopteryx* may most conveniently be shown in tabular form:

ARCHAEOPTERYX

Reptilian characters	*Avian characters*
simple brain with small cerebellum	feathers
long tail of separate vertebrae	arrangement of feathers
simple articulation of vertebrae	fused clavicles
short sacrum	pubes directed backwards
free metacarpals	opposable hallux
free metatarsal	
simple ribs	
gastralia	

If the transition from reptiles to birds was characterized by what I propose to call "mosaic evolution," it becomes of interest to enquire whether the same mode was followed in the transition between other classes of vertebrates, and to make a general investigation into the evolution of the classes of jawed vertebrates alive today.

Vertebrate animals present themselves to the eye and to the mind as disposed along five great levels, or shelves extending one above the other along the walls of time. The lowest shelf is for the fishes, the second for amphibia, the third for reptiles, and the fourth and fifth for birds and mammals. In each case, except for the last, the definition of the contents of the shelf is based on the fundamental structural and functional requirements of adaptation in a broad way to the medium or media in which the animals live. A life wholly spent in water is the governing factor for the fish; early life in water followed by life on land for the amphibia (although some may secondarily return to an aquatic existence); complete emancipation from early larval life in water for the reptiles (although some may become secondarily adapted to an aquatic medium); ability to fly in the air by means of feathers for the birds. The mammals are exposed to the same ecological problems as the reptiles, and if they are placed on a shelf above them, it is because their basic adaptation to their problems is on a level so much more efficient that an arbitrary but accepted convention has sanctioned this practice and used mammary glands and hair as diagnostic features in living forms, although it may well be that these structures were also present in the ancestors of the mammals while they were still undoubted reptiles.

In each case, only one passage from a shelf to the next has been successful and has given rise to forms which have survived as the classes of vertebrates alive today. As G. G. Simpson (1951) has stressed, it is because they have successfully survived and radiated in their newly conquered environments that these groups have become classes. If they had failed to "break-through" onto a higher shelf, like the numerous other unsuccessful competitors, they would not have given rise to a class. If the pterodactyls had established themselves in the mastery of the air, they would no doubt be regarded as a class, but they went extinct.

So firmly are the differences between the various grades of vertebrate animals impressed on the student that there is a tendency to imagine that the "hard work" of evolution consists in the transition from one shelf to that above it. There is here the possibility of error, for if evolution is measured by the quantity of change observed between the starting and ending points of a given line of descent, "more" evolution may take place on and within each shelf than in the passage from one shelf to the next. Within each shelf, evolution involves adaptive radiation which diversifies the animals to a very great extent as the different lines become more and more closely adjusted to special environments. The reptiles show this well with their astonishing diversity of form and size. Quite apart from the transitions from one shelf to the next, there is a very wide tolerance for the amount of change of size, shape, proportions, accretion or loss, which a strain of evolving animals may show.

In the case of the transitional passages from one shelf to the next, the starting and ending points of the evolutionary progress are known and definable. From one known condition the animals must have arrived at another, not very different from it but possessing a few fundamentally important characters which define the level of the next shelf.

If the method of transition from reptiles to birds, as is shown in *Archaeopteryx,* be of general applicability, it should be possible by direct appeal to the facts of observation to demonstrate its occurrence in the case of other great transitions, from fish to amphibia, from amphibia to reptiles, and from reptiles to mammals. In each case fossils are known which, although not themselves the direct ancestors of the remainder of the animals in the shelf to which the evolution is progressing, were nevertheless so closely related to them that they can be taken as examples of animals in transition. It will be of interest to consider them in a little more detail.

The Transition from Fish to Amphibian

Bony fish are alike in the possession of the following structures which not only enable them to live in their watery medium but are characteristic of them: paired fins in the form of paddles, median fins supported by cartilaginous radials and dermal fin-rays (lepidotrichia), lateral-line canals protected in tubes in the dermal bones, opercular bones protecting the branchial cavity, and a bony connexion between the hind part of the skull and the pectoral girdle. The amphibia, on the other hand, are characterized by the pentadactyl limbs; the median fins, which are found only in their aquatic forms, have no supporting radials or rays, and the lateral-line organs lie in grooves in the bones or simply in the skin, not in tubes in the bones; the bony operculum has vanished, as has the chain of bones connecting the skull with the pectoral girdle.

It is therefore remarkable that, as E. Jarvik (1952) has shown, the Ichthyostegalia present an intermediate and mixed condition in which median fins are present, supported by radials and lepidotrichia, and the lateral-line organs perforate the bones in tubes. These structures are absolutely characteristic of fish. On the other hand, the Ichthyostegalia have pentadactyl limbs, absolutely characteristic of amphibia. Less sensational than these, but nevertheless characteristic of one or the other of the two types between which the transition is made, are the following structures of Ichthyostegalia: presence of a pre-opercular bone, a (small) subopercular bone, and an ethmosphenoid bone, all of which are found in bony fish but not in amphibia; the presence of bicipital ribs, and the shortening of the hinder part of the skull which is unjointed and free from the pectoral girdle, all of which are characteristic of amphibia but not of fish.

If it were not for the pentadactyl limbs, the Ichthyostegalia would have to be regarded as fish instead of amphibia; and the fact that a single piece of the mosaic pattern marks the passage of the frontier between one class of vertebrates and another suggests that such a transition can be achieved by a moderate quantity of evolutionary change.

In his Croonian Lecture, D. M. S. Watson (1925) has already shown that the physiological and mechanical problems that required to be solved by the ancestors of the amphibia in their passage from life in water to life on land necessitated no new neurological or muscular machinery. The system of myotomes (muscle-plates) segmentally arranged on each side of the body which enables a fish to swim also enables an amphibian to crawl; the muscles of the floor of the mouth, which, by raising it when the mouth is closed, force water back into the pharynx and out through the gill-slits in the fish, also force air down into the lungs in the amphibian; the hyomandibula, which is applied to the imperforate side of the ear-capsule in fish and helps to support the upper jaw, also enables vibrations to be transmitted to the inner ear, even without the perforation of the fenestra ovalis which the most primitive amphibia have not yet achieved. In brief, the passage from class Pisces to class Amphibia involved no upheaval or sensational reconstruction of the body. This is what would be expected if the transition took place by mosaic evolution, one piece at a time.

The Ichthyostegalia present another feature of interest and general applicability, which arises out of the fact that they cannot themselves be taken as lying on the direct line of transition from the fish to the amphibia. The reason why they cannot be so regarded is that they possess some characters which are too specialized for it to have been possible for the remainder of the amphibia to have been evolved from them. Among these characters are the structure of the occipital region, and the anterior position of the articulation between the quadrate and the lower jaw. These are characters which other amphibia show at a later period of evolution, and in which the Ichthyostegalia are precociously advanced. But the fact that an animal can at one and the same time show so many features which would make it an ideal transitional form, and also spoil this picture by possessing one or two characters which rule it out as a direct ancestor, is itself an argument in support of the principle of mosaic evolution, with the different pieces evolving separately, and some of them too fast. This phenomenon is found again and again in the study of transitions from one type of animal to another, and appears to be of general applicability. It would be more difficult to understand if the transitions took place by a gradual and simultaneous conversion of all the parts of the animal.

Conversely, there are animals which in some of their features have failed to keep pace with the general progress of the group to which they belong. A case is provided by the amphibian *Eogyrinus* which is more advanced than the Ichthyostegalia in general structure and yet retains the connexion between the bones of the skull and those of the shoulder girdle which the Ichthyostegalia had already lost.

It may be of interest to have the analysis of certain characters during the transition from fish to amphibia in tabular form:

ICHTHYOSTEGA

Fish characters	*Amphibian characters*
median fin	pentadactyl limbs
radials	bicipital ribs
lepidotrichia	long forepart of skull, short hind part
pre-opercular bone	skull free from pectoral girdle
subopercular bone (vestigial)	no joint in skull
tubes for lateral line	
ethmosphenoid ossification	*Specialized characters*
short parasphenoid	structure of occipital region
	quadrate articulation too far forward

The Transition from Amphibian to Reptile

In the transition from amphibian to reptile the essential difference between them is that whereas the amphibia[1] never emancipated themselves completely from water, which is necessary for the sperm to find the egg (in the absence of internal fertilization), for the egg and larva to develop in, and for the skin to breathe, the reptiles succeeded in getting completely free from water. This they did by the evolution of copulatory organs allowing internal fertilization, the evolution of embryonic membranes (chorion, amnion, and allantois) which made it

---

[1] An exception must be made of the caecilians which, although still amphibians, have acquired independence from water by means of internal fertilization, and many of which are viviparous. They are, however, so highly specialized that they cannot be said to have made a new "shelf."

possible for the embryo to develop within a fluid medium (in the amniotic cavity) as a closed system (the cleidoic egg) inside a shell on dry land or in the oviduct; and by the acquisition of an efficient mechanism of pulmonary respiration with the ribs and intercostal muscles expanding the lungs.

The reptilian emancipation from water is reflected anatomically in the fact that the reptilian skull shows no grooves for lateral-line canals. The other structural characters diagnostic of reptiles are hard to define and involve minute details. Some of them are given in the table below.

SEYMOURIA

Amphibian characters	*Reptilian characters*
reticulate ornamentation of skull	foramen ovale large, low down, bordered by basipterygoid process
lateral-line canal grooves present	
no supra-occipital bone	lachrymal extends from orbit to nostril
large opening from braincase to inner ear	
	choanae near midline
massive paroccipital process directed upwards	articular separate from supra-angular
	basioccipital largely exposed ventrally
tubular flange covering paroccipital	large tubera basisphenoidales
palatine with tooth in pit	lower jaw hinges by articular, an independent ossification
ectopterygoid with very weak flange facing lower jaw	
shape of large pterygoid	odontoid process a single ossification
	neural arches wide and swollen
maxillary teeth with alternate replacement, with fluted roots, fused to their base and to a labial wall of bone	articular surface of zygapophyses horizontal
	digital formula 2–3–4–5–4
deep otic notch	humerus with entepicondylar foramen
intertemporal bone present	
quadrate inclined backwards	
mandible with postsplenial and three **coronoids**	
axis vertebra resembling one behind it	
intercentra with process for head of **rib**	
single sacral vertebra	
separate intermedium in tarsus	

Pre-Amphibian characters
large tooth on third coronoid
procoracoid but no coracoid

One of them is remarkable: the lower jaw hinges by means of the articular bone, an independent ossification, characteristic of no amphibian and all reptiles. *Seymouria,* which is an intermediate form long regarded as the most primitive known reptile, possesses the articular bone, but it has now been shown to have lateral-line canal grooves, and was an amphibian. It has just not got onto the new shelf. Nevertheless, D. M. S. Watson's remarks (1919, p. 291) apply with no less force than when he wrote them (before it was recognized that *Seymouria* was an amphibian): "In every part of its skeleton," he wrote, "it shows a mixture of Temnospondyl [amphibian] and Reptilian characters, each recognizable, in general showing little evidence of an intermediate condition. The whole effect of its structure is that of a mosaic of separate details, some completely amphibian, some completely reptilian, and very few, if any, showing a passage leading from one to the other."

It is clear, therefore, that the evidence from the study of the transition from amphibia to reptilia is in favour of the mosaic mode of evolution.

Seymouria also illustrates a further consequence of this type of evolution. Just as in some cases (e.g., *Ichthyostega*) an animal may show characters which have evolved too fast relative to the other characters, in other cases certain characters may have been left in a profoundly archaic condition. An example is provided in *Seymouria* by the presence of a procoracoid without a coracoid, and a large tooth on the third coronoid. These characters are those of osteolepid fish.

The Transition from Reptile to Mammal

The transition from the reptilian to the mammalian shelf of evolution is in many ways the most difficult to study. This is partly because fossils which might be regarded as ancestral to the existing mammals have not yet been found; partly because the mesozoic mammalian fossils that are known belong to unrelated groups which left no descendants; and partly because many of the features commonly accepted as characteristic of mammals were present in the group of theromorph reptiles that evolved parallel with the mammals. For example, the advanced therapsid reptiles show the following features: in the skull two occipital condyles, a bony false palate, disappearance of the pineal foramen and of the postorbital bar, appearance of turbinal bones, and a large dentary with an ascending ramus; teeth differentiated into incisors, canines, and molars, with single replacement; in the skeleton of the limbs and girdles, the loss of the cleithrum, the forward rotation of the ilium, the presence of the olecranon process on the ulna, the tuber calcis in the foot, and the reduction of the digital formula to 2-3-3-3-3; in the brain a cerebellum with vermis, flocculi, and pons Varolii.

Thanks to the work of R. Broom (1932), C.-C. Young (1947) and W. G. Kuehne, it is known that in the Triassic therapsid group of Ictidosauria, *Tritylodon* from South Africa, *Bienotherium* from China, and *Oligokyphus* from England show still closer resemblance to mammals in that their skull has lost the pre-frontal, postfrontal, and postorbital bones, the molar teeth have two roots, and the acromion process on the scapula is present. The only feature left which shows that the Therapsida, including the Ictidosauria, were still reptiles, according to the current definition, is the articulation of the lower jaw by means of the articular and quadrate bones, with the correlated condition that the columella auris was the only auditory ossicle and the angular remained in the lower jaw and had not been transformed into a tympanic bone.

The designation of the above-mentioned characters as mammalian is therefore true only when consideration is restricted to existing and living reptiles and mammals. They are not diagnostic characters and should be called mammal-like. When all the fossil forms are considered, as they must be, the only diagnostic feature of the mammals as currently accepted is the articulation of the lower jaw by means of the dentary and squamosal, and the conversion of the quadrate and articular into the incus and malleus and of the columella auris into the stapes.

Living mammals are warm-blooded and have hair which enables them to minimize the loss of heat; it is almost certain that this was also true of the higher theromorph reptiles, because of the agility which their structure argues and the presence of turbinals whose function it is to warm the air in its passage through the nose to the lungs. It is probable that these reptiles also had two ventricles, non-nucleated red blood-corpuscles, and a diaphragm, all of which are features which raise the efficiency of the circulatory and respiratory systems. What cannot be inferred from the fossilized parts, however, is whether they were viviparous, and had mammary glands, and a single left aortic arch. Judging from the monotremes, the ancestors of the mammals lacked the first of these characters but possessed the last two.

In the evolution of the other classes of vertebrates, there has in each case been a clean-cut and sudden adaptation to a new medium: the partial and total conquest of dry land, and the mastery of the air. Each of these shelves of vertebrate evolution can be characterized, therefore, not only by the diagnostic structural features, but also by a habitat. In the case of the evolution of the mammals this was not so. In the production of the mammals, there was no conquest of a new medium; primitive reptiles and mammals alike inhabited the land. Mammals are only perfected reptiles, more efficient, better adapted, and possessed of a greater degree of independence of their environment.

It follows that mammals were able to evolve slowly and gradually by progressive modifications here and there all over the body; and the point at which the distinction between reptiles and mammals is placed is purely arbitrary. In any case the diagnostic feature commonly accepted, the squamoso-dentary articulation of the lower jaw, cannot be correlated with the solution of any major problem of adaptation as was the case with the pentadactyl limb, the absence of lateral-line canal grooves, and the feathers. What this change did was to enable the mammals to chew and to hear more efficiently.

If the possession of hair were taken as the mammalian criterion, indicating a homoeothermous condition, and if it could be demonstrated in fossils, most of the higher therapsid reptiles would almost certainly be included in the mammals. The selection as a criterion of a feature which evolved late (the squamoso-dentary articulation) has had the result of relegating the important phases of mammalian evolution to the pre-mammalian stage. It follows that the reptiles among which the ancestors of mammals must be sought were already almost full of mammal-like characters. These reptiles were the Ictidosauria, and it is largely because they were Triassic and therefore too late that they cannot be regarded as directly ancestral to the mammals. The Ictidosauria must, however, have resembled these ancestral forms, and when their characters are tabulated it is seen that a few of them are fairly ancestral or reptilian while most are equally definitely progressive or mammal-like:

ICTIDOSAURIA

Ancestral reptilian characters	*Progressive mammal-like characters*
quadrate-articular articulation	two occipital condyles
columella auris simple	bony false palate
postdentary bones in lower jaw	no pineal foramen
interclavicle present	no postorbital bar
coracoid present	no pre-frontal bone
procoracoid present	no postorbital bone
	dentary large with ascending ramus
	turbinal bones
	teeth heterodont, diphyodont, molars with two roots
	no cleithrum
	olecranon process present
	acromion process present
	tuber calcis present
	ilium rotated forward
	digital formula 2–3–3–3–3
	cerebellum with vermis, flocculi, and pons Varolii

Instead, therefore, of presenting a picture in which a small number of pieces conform to the new type showing a striking mosaic, most of the pieces belong to the new type and only a few reflect the old: the mosaic has almost been converted into a self-coloured pattern.

There is another possibility of studying the transition from reptiles to mammals because there are mammals alive today which, although so highly specialized that they cannot be regarded as ancestral to any other mammals, also show a number of features which they must have inherited from the earliest mammals. These are the monotremes, and it is remarkable that they also show a mosaic of reptilian and mammalian characters, all the more interesting because they include soft parts.

Thoroughly reptilian are the oviparous type of reproduction with yolk in the egg and a shell; the presence of the egg-tooth and caruncle used for hatching; the presence of coracoids, procoracoids and inter-clavicle; and the absence of a corpus callosum from the brain.

On the other hand, the presence of hair, mammary glands, non-nucleated red blood-corpuscles, the diaphragm, single left aortic arch, squamoso-dentary articulation of the lower jaw, three auditory ossicles, and seven cervical vertebrae shows equally definite mammalian and mammal-like characters.

In other words, the monotremes have been produced from their reptilian ancestors by mosaic evolution and have remained in a condition in which some of the oldest reptilian pieces of the mosaic are preserved:

ORNITHORHYNCHUS

Reptilian characters	*Mammalian characters*
oviparous reproduction with shell and yolk	hair
	mammary glands
egg-tooth and caruncle	non-nucleated red blood-cells
squamosal canal	diaphragm
coracoid, procoracoid, interclavicle present	single left aorta
	squamoso-dentary articulation
no corpus callosum	three auditory ossicles
no pinna to ear	seven cervical vertebrae
no cribriform plate	
taenia clino-orbitalis present	

The Transition from Ape to Man

The transition from the subhuman to the human level is not only the most interesting, but perhaps the clearest, example of mosaic evolution. The starting point is the australopithecines, fossil forms that flourished in East Africa about one million years ago. A number of different specimens have been found, but unfortunately a Linnaean Latin name for a new genus or species has been given to many of them, such as *Paranthropus, Plesianthropus, Zinjanthropus, Homo habilis*. These names, and the distinctions which they are intended to convey, are not acceptable to evolutionists who know from genetics, population-studies, and comparative anatomy that in populations evolving rapidly and increasing greatly in numbers, which was the case with the australopithecines, variability is very wide, and there is no justification for ascribing the variant forms to separate genera or species, when they were only varieties of australopithecines. This is why, following Sir Wilfrid Le Gros Clark, evolutionists prefer to speak of levels: australopithecine, pithecanthropine (who was already *Homo,* many believe), and modern man. In the following table, a primitive, unspecialized form of australopithecine has been taken as a term of comparison.

A reasoned estimate of the number of individuals in the population of australopithecines one million years ago, when these man-like apes were turning into ape-like men, worked out by E. S. Deevey, is 125,000. Thereafter, it must have increased very rapidly. This is the place to remind the reader of Darwin's warning: modern man is not descended from any existing living ape, but if man's ancestor were alive today he would unquestionably be classified among the apes.

If the limb-bones of australopithecines had been found alone, they would have been regarded as human; if the molar teeth had been found alone, they would have been ascribed to an ape. Nor is this all: these ape-like creatures stood erect, as is proved by their hip-girdles and thigh-bones; and they carried their heads erect, as is shown by the forward position of the foramen magnum at the base of the skull. The evolution of man in the different parts of his body was not synchronous, and this is another definition of mosaic evolution.

AUSTRALOPITHECINE

Ape-like characters	*Man-like characters*
brain-volume small (600 c.c.)	nuchal crest low
jaws massive	small rounded forehead
jaws projecting	brain-case set high in the head
molar teeth large	foramen magnum well forward
ankle-bone head curved	teeth arranged in curved arch
	canine teeth spade-shaped
	first lower premolar small with two cusps
	type of wear in molar teeth (human method of chewing)
	form of milk-teeth
	forelimbs delicately built
	shape of hip-girdle and thigh-bone indicating vertical stance

Conclusion

It has now been seen that in the transitions between classes of living vertebrates, there is evidence that morphological evolution has progressed by means of the mode here described as mosaic. The alternative type of change, involving gradual and general conversion of the whole organism, must have occurred in regard to such characters as the chemical constitution of the body-fluids; it does not seem to have occurred in the evolutionary changes which lifted animals from one class of vertebrates to the next.

It is possible that this is connected in some way with what, following C. H. Waddington, we can call the epigenetic climate of a developing organism. Owing to the genetic make-up and the internal conditions of development in an organism, there may be only a limited number of changes possible, and it is legitimate to think that changes restricted to single organ-systems are more likely to have occurred than progressive changes affecting the entire organism. It is further probable that changes restricted to single organ-systems at a time were more viable and less likely to succumb to selection. Organisms are delicately balanced and adjusted mechanisms, and on the average, changes are more likely to upset than to strengthen them. Selection may therefore be expected to have acted with greater rigour against organisms varying in more than one direction at a time, unless the directions were correlated, as was the case with the evolution of limbs and teeth in some horses, for example.

It has long been held by palaeontologists that the different parts of organisms are capable of independent evolution, proceeding at different rates. This emerges very clearly from studies of rates of evolution as presented by G. G. Simpson (1953), and may appear to be so well known as to make this paper redundant. Perhaps it is, but it may be worth stressing that the principle of the independence of characters, shown, for example, in tooth-length and tooth-height in the evolution of the horses, also applies to the evolution of the classes of vertebrates.

A necessary consequence of mosaic evolution and of the independence of characters evolving at different rates is the production of animals showing mixtures of primitive and specialized characters.

It is a commonplace of palaeontology that in the search for ancestral forms of groups, the fossils which very nearly fill the bill usually show one or more characters that rule them out from the direct ancestry of the descendants, either because they have already lost some structure which the early members of the descendant group still have, or because they possess some structure which the early members of the group in question have not yet evolved. An example of the latter is *Ichthyostega*, where the position of the articulation of the lower jaw is more advanced than in the earliest amphibia.

In each case the fossil gives a very good approximation of the conditions that must have obtained in the real ancestor, but the picture has been spoiled by the precocious evolution of a single character or two, in which the animal anticipated the condition found in the later stages of the evolution of the group in question. A useful term to denote characters of this sort has been coined by K. P. Oakley. Following him, we may call a character in which an animal anticipates a later stage of the evolution of a group (with which it must therefore be evolving in parallel) ecgonomorphic (resembling the descendant).

Conversely, there are cases where characters have survived little-modified from the ancestral state through later stages of evolution. An example is provided by the tooth on the third coronoid of the lower jaw in *Seymouria,* in which it resembles no other known amphibian but reflects the conditions in osteolepid fish. Following E. I. White, we may call such a character progenomorphic (resembling the ancestor). The Ictidosauria as a group may be regarded as progenomorphs, for no structural features of theirs would rule them out from the ancestry of mammals if they occurred earlier in the fossil record. It must be concluded that they have preserved those ancestral features almost without change. The same may be true of *Seymouria,* which was too late to be ancestral to the reptiles.

Only in the case of *Archaeopteryx* is it permissible to say that no time-relations or structural features have yet been found to disqualify it from being regarded as ancestral to a class, viz., birds.

Finally there is the fact that one and the same animal may show primitive and specialized characters in different parts of its body. This was recognized by W. D. Matthew, who applied the term "compensation" to this condition which is, of course, only another case of mosaic evolution, in which the organism shows both ecgonomorphic and progenomorphic characters. An example is that of the Permian labyrinthodont *Trimerorhachis,* in which the condition of the occipital condyle is extremely primitive (like the Carboniferous forms), but the flattening of the skull very specialized (like the Triassic forms).

The significance and possible wide application of mosaic evolution as a general principle was suggested by D. M. S. Watson when he wrote (1919, p. 300): "The curious way in which the structure of *Seymouria* is built up of perfectly well developed amphibian characters and equally decisive reptilian features, those of intermediate type being very rare, affords a magnificent example of the way in which the evolution of great groups may have taken place." I believe that it has, and therefore propose to give to the mosaic mode of evolution the name of Watson's Rule.

CHAPTER

7

The Role of
Genetics in the Evolution
of Man

Review of *Mankind Evolving: The Evolution of the Human Species,* by Theodosius Dobzhansky, from *Scientific American,* September, 1962. Copyright © 1962 by Scientific American, Inc. All rights reserved.

Of all the natural sciences that can be brought to bear on the evolution of mankind, which is not quite the same thing as the evolution of man, genetics is among the most important and the author of this book is one of its foremost exponents. His book *Genetics and the Origin of Species* was epoch-making, and the present work is no less important. He begins by using a broad brush to sketch the scope of evolution, including that of man and his culture, and the theories advanced to explain it. Next follows an epitome of the general principles of genetics to which he has himself made such notable contributions, the relative importance of nature and nurture in determining the characters of an organism, the results of observations on identical twins, the integration of genetics and natural selection, the history of man's body as revealed by fossils, and his mental faculties and their antecedents. In a treatment of the problem of race, he shows among other things how the Indian caste system was an attempt to breed varieties of man genetically specialized to perform different functions and trades, whereas ancient China aimed at the converse process of a system of social mobility. The threats of increased mutation rates caused by the effects of radiation, and of population increase resulting from lack of control, come in for careful appraisal; and although these dangers are squarely faced, and self-awareness is recognized as a blessing in giving man the power of imagination but as a curse in accompanying this gift with those of responsibility and freedom, the note on which he ends is not one of despair. Instead, his discussion constantly provokes thought, which is obviously the first step along the way to the solution of these problems.

The significance of a hereditary link between the human race and the animal kingdom was already recognized by Darwin in the earliest notebook entries that he made in 1837, within a year of his return to England from the voyage of the *Beagle*. At that time he wrote: "If we choose to let conjecture run wild, then animals, our brethren in pain, disease, death, suffering and famine—our slaves in the most laborious works, our companions in our amusements—they may partake of our origin in one common ancestor—we may be all netted together." It is through genetics that we are all netted together in evolution, although at the time Darwin wrote these words knowledge of genetics amounted to less than nothing. The theory of blending inheritance, all that there then was to go on, is utterly false. It held that offspring struck an average between the characters of their parents and that variation was therefore halved after each generation. With the application of the experimental method to problems of heredity, first by Gregor Mendel and then by Thomas Hunt Morgan and his colleagues, the science of genetics has now been placed on an unassailable basis, and heredity has its particulate genes, just as physics and chemistry have their elemental particles, quanta and atoms. Realization of the implications of the principles of genetics remains, however, astonishingly poor among laymen.

It is still said, for instance, that a son is a chip off the old block. It may be that he resembles his father, but if he does, it is not because he is a detached bit of him, as is commonly imagined. Children are not the products of their parents at all. If they were, it would be impossible to understand why brothers or sisters are not identical; after all, their ancestry is identical. It would be necessary to suppose that all the differences between them were the result of new variations that had arisen during their own lives. Genetics has to account for differences no less than similarities; the problem is as simple—and as fundamental—as that. Children are the products of the germ plasm, the stream of hereditary factors that has flowed through the ancestors containing the genes, of which parents are nothing but the custodians who were themselves formed from the germ plasm of their antecedents. Children are the delayed brothers and sisters of their parents, and from the beginning of the evolution of man on earth it is literally and scientifically true that all men are brothers.

Because of the peculiar mechanism by which germ cells—eggs and sperm—are formed, no child can contain more than half of the genes carried by either parent. The mother is as likely as the father to transmit genes controlling characters that in some instances are shown by neither parent. Furthermore, the same mechanism of germ-cell formation sees to it that the complement of genes received by a child is not identical with that of either parent. There is plenty of room for the possibility that the chip may differ significantly from the old block, and this is what makes it difficult to support the view that the qualities of a useful legislator, say, are bound to appear in his children. For the same reason schemes to establish a sperm bank in which the most distinguished men would have accounts cannot avoid an element of chance. If you breed 10,000 peas or fruit flies, differing in characters controlled by genes that have been analyzed, the proportions in which the offspring will show those characters can be predicted with fair accuracy; when it comes to one child produced by one man and one woman, it is more difficult. Furthermore, as Professor Dobzhansky cogently asks, "Are we ready to agree what the ideal man ought to be?" Besides, there is something more, because there is another notion that is in need of repair. It is the view, still often expressed, that some characters are "innate" and others are "acquired." Nothing would seem to be more innate than that vertebrate animals should have two eyes in their heads. They have had them since the Silurian period, 350 million years ago. Yet if a fish embryo is made to develop in water to which a small quantity of a simple salt such as magnesium chloride has been added, it does not develop a pair of eyes at all but a single eye in the middle of its head like a Cyclops. This is one of the proofs that regardless of how long a time a line of ancestors may have possessed genes that control the development of structures, they cannot produce normal structures if the environment is abnormal. The reason for this is that the development of any character whatever is the result of interaction between the genes inside the organism and the factors of the environment outside it. Conversely, those people who set great store by the action of the environment must be reminded by this same simple experiment that 350 million years of normal environment has done nothing to "fix" the invariable and normal development of characters that one might think had been as irrevocably built in as a pair of eyes.

What all this adds up to is that every character that any plant or animal develops has its basis in the genes (without which it would not develop at all and is to that extent "inherited"; but because the character is the result of interaction between the genes and the factors of the environment, it is also to that extent "acquired." There is no such thing as a character that owes its existence solely to heredity or solely to environment. All that is inherited by any offspring is a packet of genes with the capacity of reacting in various ways to the environment, and a few of these ways, within a certain latitude of tolerance in a normal environment, are what are regarded as normal. Some of the genes, possessed of what is called a high degree of penetrance, can overcome a wider range of variation in environmental factors than others and show their effects. This is at the base of the old controversy between "nature" and "nurture," opposed to which it is necessary to regard both nature and nurture as cooperating, without our being able to say in any one case exactly how much has been contributed by either.

The extent to which nurture undoubtedly can affect the end product of development is sometimes astonishing, and it is well illustrated by the history of Clarence and Timmy, sparrows described on page 73. This surely is one of the most awe-inspiring facts that have come to light, if what was never thought to be anything more than a stupid little creature weighing only a few grams is capable of such a degree of mental development and friendship. Could all sparrows, to say nothing of other passerine birds, become like Clarence and Timmy if they were brought up in similar human environments? St. Francis of Assisi would surely have agreed, and Darwin would have rejoiced at being netted together with Clarence and Timmy.

There can be few matters affecting man as a social organism that do not depend for their solution on a scientific appreciation of the nature-nurture problem. As Professor Dobzhansky points out, eugenics is, as conceived by some of its exponents, in danger of being a travesty of science through overreaching itself by exaggerating the influence of heredity, and for the opposite reason psychoanalysis is in comparable danger from failure to recognize the part played by heredity. If Freud had appreciated the objectively based principles of genetics and the part heredity plays in psychology, if he had freed himself from his Lamarckian blinkers and the discredited theory of recapitulation, and if he had been less prone to make assumptions about birth traumas, sex drives and Oedipus complexes, there might be less controversy over what was started as a therapeutic technique and has come to be regarded as a pattern of life with ramifications extending into history, sociology and religion.

It is one of the worst injustices of history that Lamarck's name is not used to designate evolution, of which he was the first to put forward a general scheme. Instead, "Lamarckism" is used to express concepts such as the supposed inheritance of acquired characters and of the effects of use and disuse of organs, ideas of which he was not the originator and which have been shown to be false. From what has been said above of the relation between heredity and environment in the development of characters, it can readily be seen that the expression "inheritance of acquired characters" has as much meaning as the saying "Caesar and Pompey were very much alike, especially Pompey." It is not surprising that this folk belief should be so old and so persistent because, as the University of Pennsylvania botanist Conway Zirkle has aptly shown, it is based on two propositions each of which by itself is approximately correct. The first is that under the influence of the environment the body of an organism can be made to undergo changes, such as a thickening of the skin where it is subjected to friction or a strengthening of muscles that are in hard use. The second proposition is that like tends to beget like. But when the two propositions are combined into a sort of syllogism, the conclusion is fallacious that parents, after having been modified by the environment, beget offspring that show the same modification in the absence of the environmental factors that originally called it forth. Many people can say that "it stands to reason" that acquired characters should be inherited; but it happens not to stand to fact, as virtually countless experiments have shown. The extent to which this fallacy is deep-seated can be seen in the Old Testament story of Jacob and Laban described on page 90. One wonders if Pauline theologians realize that the doctrine of original sin involves the inheritance of an acquired character, for only genes can be inherited and, by the nature of the case, neither Adam nor Eve when they first appeared on the scene possessed the character they are alleged to have transmitted to all their descendants. It is perhaps unkind to drive this last lesson home to its conclusion, but everything known about evolution shows it to be a process that takes place in populations numerous enough to ensure that interchange of genes is widespread and frequent enough to provide a sufficient supply of variation for natural selection to work on. As mentioned on pages 102 and 112, it has been computed that the population of man's ancestors one million years ago was about 125,000 individuals. That was when man was emerging from his pre-human ancestors and no doubt was in many ways very brutal, so that mankind would have started with 125,000 doses of genes predisposing toward behaviour that would now be regarded as sinful.

Great as the importance of genetics is in the pageant of evolution because of the part it has played in such continuity as there has been, there are three other actors of no less significance. The first is variation, concerning which Darwin wrote with simple truth that its causes were in his day completely unknown. It is one of the triumphs of genetics that this question can now be answered at a different level by saying that the causes of heritable variation are known; they are the mutation of genes due to fortuitous rearrangement of the contents of the genetic material, and the recombination of genes through sexual reproduction. This results in numbers of possible permutations of such astronomical magnitude that infinitely more variation is potentially possible than is ever realized.

The next actor is adaptation, sometimes called fitness. There is no such thing as adaptation in a vacuum. A plant or animal is adapted in varying degrees to a particular set of environmental conditions—a habitat or place that it is useful to call an ecological niche.

The last actor is natural selection. At the time Professor Dobzhansky delivered the lectures that form the subject matter of his book, he had had no opportunity to become familiar with the contents of the manuscript notebooks in which Darwin recorded his thoughts and conclusions soon after his return from the voyage of the *Beagle;* it is only recently that I have provided an authentic version of these notebooks. As a result Professor Dobzhansky, like everyone else, has been slightly misled by the ambiguous phrasing of the passage in Darwin's autobiography in which he wrote that it was on reading Thomas Malthus's *An Essay on the Principle of Population* he had at once been struck that favourable variations would tend to be preserved and unfavourable ones to be destroyed. This remark has been generally construed to mean that Darwin derived his theory of natural selection from Malthus. It has always been difficult to understand how Darwin could have been indebted for the key of evolution to Malthus, the Jeremiah who maintained that the social state of man was unimprovable. Darwin's notebooks show that he had thought out for himself the unlimited possibility of variation, the importance of niches in the economy of nature and the principle of natural selection before he ever opened Malthus's book. Darwin began to read Malthus on September 28, 1838, and what he got from it was the realization that natural selection exerts a pressure that forces those individuals who happen to have the requisite characters into the niches and leaves the others outside. Malthus knew nothing of, and did not want to know anything of, unlimited variation, ecological niches or natural selection; all that he supplied to Darwin was the argument, already known to Sir William Petty and Benjamin Franklin, that the reproductive rate unchecked outstrips food supply and that mortality must therefore be high. Nobody but Darwin integrated the facts of extinction, variation, geographical distribution, ecological niches and natural selection into a system that showed how natural selection exerts pressure resulting in adaptation. Professor Dobzhansky has interesting and profound things to say on the nature of creative thought, which, he thinks, may be a greater mystery to the creative poet or scientist than to his biographer.

Natural selection still operates in man and in some respects may become more rigorous, but for the most part its effects are nullified by the evolution of an ethical social system that is the one exclusive feature of man. Professor Dobzhansky agrees on the importance of paedomorphosis in the emergence of man, but he is concerned to know how it was achieved by natural selection. As I believe I was the first to generalize this subject a third of a century ago, I hope I may be allowed to suggest that the array of variants, on which natural selection acts, includes not only adult genetic variants but also variants along the time scale of development, some of which may be more juvenile and better adapted than others. The effect of slowing down the rate of bodily development is to allow for such features as more brain growth before the skull sutures close and to make the early postnatal stages so helpless that a prolonged period of parental care is necessary. During this time a character of "authority-acceptance" on the part of the children, as the University of Edinburgh geneticist C. H. Waddington has suggested, confers survival value, because without it the children would inevitably come to grief more than they do. The long period of childhood and parental care consolidated the family as a social unit that tended to become monogamous as woman became uninterruptedly receptive, and it provided a long period of overlap between generations during which experience could be taught. This process, which is not enforced by genetic inheritance, has to be repeated at the start of each generation and is the basis of what Professor Dobzhansky calls superorganic evolution and Sir Julian Huxley calls psychosocial evolution. It is responsible for the origin and maintenance of civilization and culture; man could not live without it. It is vastly more efficient than biological evolution as an instrument to bring about adaptation in man, and the speed with which it works is not only much faster but also is still accelerating. Yet it has not annulled the underlying genetic mechanism of evolution that still determines such matters as the response of the individual to the environment, even if it is the result of civilization.

Nobody would wish for a geneticist dictator even if his name were Plato, but it would do legislators no harm to appreciate the genetic effect of their policies. One cannot help wondering how many of them do, in any country. They might say that there are two cultures, humanities and science, and that there is no time to learn both. This would be no answer. There is only one culture, but most people are not even half-cultured.

CHAPTER

8

The World of
an Evolutionist

Review of *This View of Life* by George Gaylord Simpson,
from *Science,* volume 143, March, 1964. Copyright © 1964
by the American Association for the Advancement of
Science.

Nearly forty years ago I took out of their glass case in the Oxford
University Museum the specimens of Mesozoic mammals from Stones-
field so that they might be studied by a young visiting scientist from
the United States, George Gaylord Simpson. Since that day, in common with all biologists, I have followed with increasing wonder and
admiration the ever-deepening debt in which he has placed his colleagues
by his researches and his interpretation of their significance for the central problem in science, life, of which the most basic aspect is evolution.
Since the work under review—*This View of Life* (Harcourt, Brace,
and World, New York, 1964), by George Gaylord Simpson—is in
some respects autobiographical, it is pertinent to look back on that time.
The 1920's were a bewildering period for biologists. A year after the

publication of T. H. Morgan's cast-iron proof that genes are carried in linear order in chromosomes, I remember arguing with W. Bateson, who refused to accept it and sank himself into more and more impossible positions with his presence-and-absence hypothesis. Mendelian geneticists, who ascribed evolution to mutation but were utterly unable to account for adaptation, pointed scornful fingers at Darwinian selectionists because their own toy, mutation, provided the only evidence of heritable variation, in clear-cut steps, without selection playing any part in the process. Darwinian selectionists parried the attack by protesting that such mutations as were then known differed from the insensible gradations that Darwin had postulated and were either deleterious or even lethal. A third group called down a plague on both the other houses and marched behind a banner bearing Lamarck's name, refusing to admit any other cause for evolution than the inheritance of acquired characters by impressed effect of environmental factors, remanence of habitudinal innovations, use and disuse. Even P. Kammerer's suicide, after G. K. Noble had shown that his experimental demonstrations had been fraudulently faked by injecting newts' hands with Indian ink (and on the wrong side), had no effect on the Neo-Lamarckians, and the three-sided contest continued acrimoniously, aimlessly, and unprofitably, like a ship with neither compass nor chart but with three captains, until an unexpected thing happened.

Brought up in the Mendelian school, R. A. Fisher started to make experiments in genetics. To his astonishment he found that the phenotypic effect of any given gene was under the control of the other genes of what came to be called the gene-complex of an organism, whose action modified the said phenotypic effect in one way or another, and modified it *gradually* in a few generations. A gene that determines a dominant character does so as a result of a reshuffling of the gene-complex in such a way as to allow the gene in question to show its effect even when in the heterozygous state. This happens when this effect is beneficial to the organism. But reshuffling involves the production of many different gene-complexes, some of which produce viable organisms while others do not, and the gene in question has *become* dominant by gradual steps under selection. Conversely, a gene *becomes* recessive if its effect in the prevailing environment is deleterious, again as a result of selection. E. B. Ford then showed that, by selecting along different lines, one and the same gene can be made dominant in one strain and recessive in another. In other words, at the very heart of Mendelian genetics, Fisher found incontrovertible evidence for selection. Further, his mathematical analysis of selection showed that no gene has any chance of establishing itself in the wild type of a population if the slightest degree of selection is exerted against it, and that in nature the vast majority of mutations *are* acted upon adversely by selection under the conditions obtaining when they mutated, which is why so many of them are recessive.

This observation also shows that there is no "favourable breeze" of mutations with immediately beneficial effects, such as those on which upholders of programmed theories of evolution rest their case—"every theory of evolution which assumes, as do all theories alternative to natural selection, that evolutionary changes can be explained by some hypothetical agency capable of controlling the nature of the mutations that occur, is involving a cause which demonstrably would not work, even if it were known to exist." That put "paid" to the account of the Neo-Lamarckians and that of many other philosophers, and it meant that Darwinians and Mendelians had been fighting one another for groundless reasons; the two schools were then integrated, and the synthetic theory of evolution emerged, as if by magic, out of the seemingly hopeless muddle.

The last word on the credibility and course of evolution lies with the palaeontologists, and this was where Simpson came in. Before him, palaeontologists were prone to draw conclusions from inadequate evidence which they did not hesitate to write into grandiloquent theories. Because Cuvier found that a fauna appeared suddenly in a stratum and vanished completely in the next, he advocated special creation of that fauna at the start of the period of time represented by that stratum and a catastrophe at its end. After evolution was accepted, A. Hyatt was led to provide "proof" of the theory of recapitulation, and other men of "orthogenesis." It is against this background of confusion, conclusions drawn from incomplete evidence, and muddled principles that the significance of Simpson's work emerges.

This is not the place to go into the details of his massive contributions to palaeontology and taxonomy. It must suffice to say that as a result of minute attention to extensive material, he has shown that evolution is causally determined but not predetermined, and that its course has been opportunistic. To take one example, rigorous analysis of the history of the horse reveals that, instead of what had previously been thought to be a trend in a single constant direction, there have been several trends in as many different directions and that the horse of today has only become what he is as a result of a zigzag course followed by his ancestors, with respect to their toes, their teeth, and their sizes. This was not the fulfillment of any programme but the result of opportune variations in directions, which at various times enabled the animals to cope with unpredictable changed conditions and so to escape the extinction that overtook all those forms that persisted too long in the directions of their old lines. Here was palaeontology providing evidence for adaptation and selection. It became even stronger when the rate of evolution was found not to be correlated with the degree of variability shown by the evolving animals, nor with the length of time occupied by a generation. The result has been that, thanks to Simpson, palaeontology provides the coping stone of the synthetic theory of evolution.

But Simpson is not only a palaeontologist. Rare among his colleagues, he has made himself master of *all* the disciplines involved in the synthetic theory, and particularly of taxonomy, which makes him a great biologist. He is not only a biologist but a man of science with the widest horizon and experience. He recognizes that science is an exploration of the material universe which seeks natural, orderly relationships among observed phenomena and that it is self-testing. It is a mistake to think that prediction is the only way of testing hypotheses. Science and the unification of science, he believes, can be meaningfully sought not through principles that apply to all phenomena, but through phenomena to which all principles apply. This pregnant inversion reappears in the passage where he says that he does not think evolution supremely important because it is his speciality, but that, on the contrary, it is his speciality because he thinks it supremely important, not only for the extension of scientific knowledge, but to make so-called educated people aware of the nature of the world into which Darwin led them, out of the world in which Thomas Jefferson could deny that any species had become extinct and John Wesley could assert that there were no earthquakes before Adam and Eve were chased out of Eden because they had acquired a character, sin, which so many still believe to have been inherited.

To a British scientist it comes as something of a shock to realize the opposition to the teaching of evolution in the United States. In Britain this is not so among teachers or teaching authorities; there is of course the odd crank who raves against evolution because it is not "scriptural" (by which token he should also believe that the earth is flat with water underneath and the sun revolving around it), but otherwise there is no opposition, only apathy and ignorance. Two hundred and forty randomly selected television viewers were recently invited by the BBC to say what name they associated with evolution. Only one-third of that number had the idea that Darwin was an answer to the question.

But Simpson is not only a man of science; he understands and defines what it is. His chapter on the historical factor in science should be prescribed reading for all scientists, especially for those who claim that their science is "exact." The beautifully clear distinction drawn between "non-historical" and "historical" events in the universe, their relation to the "immanent" and "configurational" aspects of matter, the bearing of these relations on the great principles of uniformitarianism, predictability, emergence of new properties, extrapolation of trends, and the meaning of "explanation" brings simple order into a chaos of muddled thinking. Deans of arts faculties should not miss this inspired analysis either, for human history and sociology also come under the beam of its light. The sciences form a spectrum from physics, where the historical aspect of events is ignored and sometimes denied, to sociology, where the historic aspect is greatest and the non-historical is sometimes denied. "Unfortunately philosophers of science have tended to concentrate on one end of this spectrum, and that the simplest, so much as to give a distorted, in some instances quite false, idea of the philosophy of science as a whole." This is part of the unbalance that results from the "hegemony of physics" in the sciences. At the other end of the scale, there have been men, including Teilhard de Chardin, who have honestly deceived themselves into believing that they could and did achieve an integration of science with mysticism. In showing up the internal contradictions and inconsistencies amounting to double talk in such efforts, the acuteness and trenchancy of Simpson's analysis disposes once and for all of the pretensions of these works' authors that they have any claim to being science, without prejudice (so gentle is Simpson even in opposition) to their excellence as essays in mysticism.

A curious feature of the study of evolution has been the tardiness with which some of the most promising avenues of research (as recognized by hindsight) have been explored. Biologists are now aware of the paradox that Darwin owed his achievement largely to observation of nature in the field, but when the impact of his great breakthrough was realized, biologists rushed indoors to the dissecting dishes and microscopes and neglected nature in the field and in the breeding pen, where they have since fulfilled Darwin's prophecy that in about fifty years evidence for evolution by natural selection should be obtained, a prophecy that, towards the end of his life, Darwin made to his son Leonard. There is a pattern in this comedy which allows men to play for years with the very tools that will open the safe of knowledge without their realizing that they have the keys in their hands. Lyell and Blyth knew the ingredients out of which Darwin distilled the mechanism of evolution by natural selection, but they failed to see their significance because of their preference for theological orthodoxy. Darwin himself obtained genetical results from his breeding experiments analogous to those from which Mendel extracted the laws of particulate inheritance, which Darwin was unable to grasp because he was so deeply imbued with the correlated wholeness of the organism. Bateson had access to the facts which Fisher wove into the integration of genetics with selection, but Bateson passed them by while being driven into positions more and more untenable. As A. N. Whitehead remarked, "Everything of importance has already been said by someone who did not discover it." This is the pattern of the history of science.

There is another aspect of tardiness which is due to what Claude Bernard meant when he wrote, "It is what we think we know that prevents us from learning." Until recently biologists thought they knew exactly how Darwin came by his theory of natural selection, but they misunderstood his *Autobiography* (not entirely their fault), and his *Notebooks* had to wait a hundred years after the publication of the *Origin of Species* before they were subjected to close scrutiny and the correct answer was found. Another basic consequence of Darwin's achievement had to wait the same time—the purposiveness of adaptation. As a fact, it is undeniable, and it was interpreted by Paley (and by other last-ditchers since then) to mean that teleological final causes, pre-ordained programs, and providential (not to say divine) guidance were at work, an interpretation that led to a head-on collision between theologians and scientists as in the battles of Oxford and Dayton. Asa Gray praised Darwin for bringing teleology back into science because adaptation is purposive. But what Darwin really did was to show that organs which serve a purpose can and do arise, without any preceding agent of purposefulness at all but opportunistically, by the rigorously nonrandom directives of natural selection. This conclusion is inescapable now that it is known that the vast majority of species which have lived on earth have become extinct (was this providential guidance?) and that the vast majority of new heritable variations are acted upon adversely by selection (thereby wrecking any preordained program).

The term "teleology" was the trouble because of its metaphysical, not to say theological, connotation with which men of science were, of course, unable to compromise. Here it is fitting to recall the words of a forgotten mathematician from Cambridge (England), William Kingdon Clifford, who in 1875 pointed out the confusion that arises from the two meanings ascribed to the concept of purpose. In the first, the idea of the end precedes the use of the means as in theological teleology. In the second, an adaptation may serve a purpose even if it originated by accident, "by processes of natural selection." Clifford went on to say that "since the process of natural selection has been understood, *purpose* has ceased to suggest design to instructed people, except in cases where the agency of man is independently probable." This luminous analysis was, however, neglected, and the *Origin of Species* had to wait a hundred years for Colin Pittendrigh to clarify what Darwin meant by introducing the valuable term "teleonomic," a term that does not antagonize scientists as teleology does.

Is Simpson right in drawing a distinction between the concept of differential mortality and survival, to which he restricts Darwin's view of selection, and reproductive selection, which means the consistent production of more offspring? It is true that in the later editions of the *Origin* Darwin made the mistake of adopting Herbert Spencer's unfortunate expression "survival of the fittest" when (rightly) dissatisfied with the adequacy of his own term "natural selection." He would have been better advised to turn to his *Notebook* of 1838 and use the words with which he committed to paper the flash of light that struck him on 28 September of that year: "One may say there is a force like a hundred thousand wedges trying to force every structure into the gaps in the oeconomy of nature, or rather forming gaps by thrusting out weaker ones." It is also true that Darwin frequently speaks of survival as the prize won by adequate adaptations, but this is always shorthand to mean survival in order to leave offspring, for he never lost sight of the fact that differential reproduction is the effective element in selection. As he wrote in the *Origin,* "I use the term struggle for existence in a large and metaphorical sense . . . including (which is more important) not only the life of the individual, but success in leaving progeny" (Peckham's *Variorum* edition, p. 146). I may also add that as David Lack has shown, it is deleterious for a species to produce too many offspring, because their ecological conditions may lead to the consequences that are now seen in many underdeveloped nations. I therefore prefer Darwin's guarded expression "success in leaving offspring."

CHAPTER
9

At the Edge of Science

Review of *The Discovery of Time* by Stephen Toulmin
and June Goodfield, from *The New York Review of Books*,
June, 1966.

In universities where they are taught, there are two subjects which
are usually combined into one department—the history of science and
the philosophy of science—and they can make strange bedfellows. The
history of science, reconstructing the problems with which great men of
science of the past were confronted, and paying due attention to the
state of knowledge then attained, studies the way in which they solved
those problems, if necessary repeating the observations and the experiments which they made. Such studies can be as objective as the work
that they retrace; in a sense they are verifications of old data, and can
qualify as science.

With the philosophy of science, the situation can be different. One
distinguished leader in this field has said that scientific observations

and experiments do not really tell us anything about the universe, but only suggest to us how to draw a picture of the universe. The trouble with this is that it lets the door wide open to considerations which are not scientific but subjective. This is how there has come to be a Roman Catholic philosophy of science, of which Galileo once fell foul, which placed Montesquieu's and Erasmus Darwin's works on the Index of prohibited books, and which has still not reconciled itself to facts of human ecology. On the other side there has arisen a Marxist history of science in the name of which Nicolai Ivanovitch Vavilov was murdered and a whole science—genetics—for a time stifled. These are some of the reasons why scientists are suspicious of the philosophy of science, for since the conclusions to which it comes can rarely be subjected to experimental tests, it may be philosophy but may also not be science.

And yet the problem cannot be shrugged off easily. However hardheaded and objective the scientist may be in the laboratory, the time always comes when he must make sense of his results. In any scientific discipline—say chemistry—it is usually the case that the data can be arranged in the framework of more than one hypothesis. Eventually, if he is lucky, the scientist decides on one of these hypotheses in preference to the others. Was the reason why he preferred that hypothesis to the others a chemical reason? No; it was because, in his view, it accorded with more data than did the others, and encountered fewer obstacles. In other words, it seemed to him to approximate more closely to—to what? We must avoid saying "to the truth," because that may involve a moral judgment, but we can say, to the accurate description of whatever phenomenon of nature was being studied. This preference for refinement of accuracy is not itself chemical; nor was the preference for the Copernican as opposed to the Ptolemaic system itself astronomical; nor is the preference for the theory of evolution by natural selection of heritable variation, over the mysticism of special creation, itself biological. What has come in here is a sense of values, not in themselves scientific, which is basic to all intellectual activity. This, I suppose, is philosophy; and it must have been the reason why Sir Winston Churchill once said at the Massachusetts Institute of Technology: "How right you are to have a Dean of Humanities." Philosophy as the servant of objective science, not a flying horse for metaphysical speculation.

These prolegomena have been introduced so as to try to come to some conclusion about which shelf in the library the book under review belongs to. I may be accused of cowardice when I suggest that there should be two copies of it: one in general philosophy, and the other in the history of science, and I expect a ton of bricks from the protagonists of the philosophy of science who will claim that this book rightly belongs to them.

It is learned, well-constructed, fine-grained, and closely argued, yet eminently readable. It sets out to place the genealogies of ideas, treated in the authors' previous volumes, into their historical contexts, and to generalize about the interchange between scientific thought and "culture." By "discovery of time" is meant the addition of this dimension to those of space in attempts to interpret the universe; and this implies the intrusion of what is called "history" into studies of the universe.

The authors claim to have made two discoveries. The first is that there has been a close parallel in the growth of historical consciousness across a whole range of subjects as widely separated as physical cosmology and theology or sociology, a conclusion which shows how they have found themselves led to step off limits from the natural sciences into other fields of intellectual inquiry that are usually separated from science, such as the humanities. The second relates to the recurrence of patterns of theory in a number of disciplines (they call them "historical sciences") which have faced common forms of problems with similar methods of solving them, such as the establishment of well-founded temporal sequences of past epochs. With all this on the plate, I fear that a really adequate review of such a book is barely possible without going some way toward answering the Chinese examination paper which has only one question: comment on all you know.

The pageant advances majestically from the speculations of the Greeks, through myths, the Scriptures and their heavy hand, the Renaissance, the emergence of natural science, the *philosophes,* and the geologists, to Darwin, who forced a pedigree on life with consequences to human thought which have still not been squarely faced, let alone fully fathomed. Throughout, the treatment is objective, and neither politicians nor theologians will find much grist for their mills in it. I have found only one point in it which I know to be incorrect, and I shall describe it, if only in order to show how high the standard of the authors' accuracy is. Jean Etienne Guettard was the first (although he slid back later), in 1751, to recognize the volcanic nature of rocks in the centre of France, and the discovery was important because it clipped the wings of the "Neptunists," who attributed everything in the Earth's crust to the effects of Noah's Flood. Guettard was accompanied on this memorable journey from Paris, through Vichy, to Volvic, by Chrétien-Guillaume de Lamoignon de Malesherbes, that great statesman who was afterwards guillotined for having served as defense counsel to Louis XVI. But Guettard was a man who made enemies; his work was denigrated, his priority denied, and a curious story gained credence (also with the present authors) that it was on his return from Vesuvius (where he never went), going up the Rhône at Montélimar, that his attention was drawn to the volcanic nature of rocks by the paving blocks in the roadway. In itself, this false story has not the slightest importance, except to provide an example of how error can be grafted in the place of truth and incorporated in "history" (see *Annals of Science,* vol. 18, 1962, p. 49, for details of this little story). Such mistakes can be serious, however, as when Friedrich Wöhler is credited (but not by these authors) with having synthetized urea in 1828, and broken down the barrier between inorganic and organic chemistry. It was no synthesis but a decomposition, for Wöhler started from blood, horns, and hooves, and made no claim to have broken a barrier, only to have obtained urea without a kidney, musing on the fact that it was necessary to start from materials taken from a living organism (see D. McKie, *Nature,* London, vol. 153, 1944, p. 608).

Perhaps the most interesting but intractable problems raised in the mind of the reader of this book relate to the meaning of the words "history" and "historical sciences." The authors quote R. G. Collingwood's definition that only human beings, not nature, have history, because the historian is concerned with the motives of the people who have played a part in the events which are called history. On this view, cosmology, geology, and biology cannot qualify as "historical" sciences. To this, the authors point out that human and non-human history share certain methods of inquiry, and that their common features are more significant than their differences. They claim, for example, that archaeology plays a large part in history, and that archaeological methods cannot be sharply distinguished from those of geology. I wonder, particularly when I see Sir Isaiah Berlin writing (*Historical Inevitability,* Oxford, 1954, p. 52):

History is not identical with imaginative literature, but it is certainly no more free from what, in a natural science, would rightly be condemned as unwarrantably subjective or personal. Except on the assumption that history must deal with human beings purely as material objects in space—must, in short, be behaviorist—its method can scarcely be assimilated to the standards of an exact natural science. The invocation to historians to suppress even that minimal degree of psychological evaluation which is necessarily involved in viewing human beings as creatures with purposes and motives (and not merely as causal factors in the procession of events), seems to me to rest upon a confusion of the aims and methods of the humane studies with those of natural science. It is one of the greatest and most destructive fallacies of the last hundred years.

Arising out of this problem is another, which has recently been treated by George Gaylord Simpson as "the historical factor in science" (*This View of Life;* see above, p. 161). Starting from the definition of history as "change through time," Simpson has no difficulty in showing that it is inadequate. A chemical reaction in a test-tube results in change through time, but is not an historical event such as was Newton's observation of the fall of an apple. The chemical reaction has always occurred and will always occur; Newton's observation was non-recurrent, it was the result of previous events in Newton's life and the cause of other events in the lives of Newton's successors. The chemical reaction is non-historical; Newton's observation was historical. Non-historical events are immanent in the material universe; historical events are configurational. The fascinating thing is that a science such as biology can contain both non-historical and historical components. Molecular biology is immanent and non-historical; palaeontology is configurational and historical. This distinction has bearings of the highest importance on the great principles of uniformitarianism, predictability, emergence of new properties, and extrapolation of trends.

So there are non-historical sciences and historical sciences, and both types occur, though to different extents, in the various branches of science as traditionally defined. In the spectrum starting from physics and passing through chemistry, astronomy, geology, biology, anthropology, psychology, and sociology, the historical element is least in physics and greatest in sociology (which is why it is not universally accepted as a science). Nevertheless, it would be incorrect to conclude that non-historical sciences are concerned solely with immanent properties, and historical sciences only with configurations, because "explanation" in the historical sciences includes all the relevant facts of the non-historical sciences involved. Biological evolution includes the immanent items of atomic and molecular properties.

This is some measure of the depths of the waters through which the authors of the present book navigate with skill and grace. They stimulate, too.

As ethology improves our understanding of animal behavior, we may acquire something of the same insight into the outraged feelings of territorial possession that set the Roman geese cackling on the Capitoline Hill. Human motives, after all, are not entirely unique. Thus, in the last resort, what marks human history off from natural history is the fact that it is—quite deliberately—man-centered. The motives of the Capitoline geese are interesting to the Roman historian only for their effect on the human city: we can leave the geese themselves to write their own goose-history.

But was it their innate sense of territory that set the geese cackling, and not sheer funk at unusual noises? It would be interesting to devise an experiment to test not only how intense is a goose's sense of territorial possession, but also what the stimuli are to which it responds by cackling. But this is science, and it suggests one last problem which crosses the mind of at least one reader of this book: We have had a definition of history, and we have seen that there are non-historical sciences and historical sciences. What, then, is science itself?

Science, in English, for the last hundred years has meant the natural sciences, and this limitation must be due to the fact that the material benefits conferred by applications of physics, chemistry, biology, and medicine to men's lives on the material plane have been greater than the uncertain advantages that have accrued from theology, history, or philosophy. John Ruskin struggled hard to resist this limitation of the word "science," and in 1875 he argued that "there is a science of Morals, a science of History, a science of Grammar, a science of Music, and a science of Painting: and all these are quite beyond comparison higher fields for human intellect, and require accuracies of intenser observation, than either chemistry, electricity, or geology" (*Works,* vol. 22, p. 396, London, 1906). Poor Ruskin, the worst advocate possible for achieving his object.

Just as mistaken as Ruskin are those who think that science can be defined in terms of what they call "the scientific method" of observation and experiment, which scientists use, and which have given such outstandingly successful results. So they have, but they can be and are also used in epigraphy, palaeography, numismatics, bibliography, genealogy, and linguistics. Even philately can benefit; after the philatelist has brought observation to bear on the stamp which is the object of his study, he performs an experiment by applying alcohol to the back of his stamp to reveal its otherwise invisible watermark. The so-called "scientific method" is not restricted to "science," which has no monopoly on it.

What, then, is science? Karl Popper has called it the field of intellectual endeavour in which propositions can be disproved but never proved, a conclusion to which he has said that he came when contemplating the fact that Newton's system was overtaken and displaced by Einstein's. Such an asymmetrical concept of the confidence to be attached to hypotheses is no doubt useful, but it makes one wonder whether the tragedy of a beautiful theory killed by an ugly fact is really so general in the progress of science. Science progresses by refinement rather than by revolution, but this has still not yet told us what science is. Simpson has defined it as an exploration of the universe that seeks natural and orderly relationships among observed phenomena, and that is self-testing. May we add that it is the result of application of the so-called "scientific method" to the products of nature, the only material out of which this method can extract general principles of universal validity? The watermark on a stamp may establish a fact, but no general principle.

It has become fashionable, but I believe misguided, to refer to intellectual activity in Western civilization as split between two so-called cultures. In fact, the culture that has blossomed in Western civilization is so rich that it has spread into a much larger number of streams than two, among which, unfortunately, the exigencies of education have not provided the opportunities for interchange and cross-fertilization which are desirable. But in the liberal arts as in the sciences, the mental processes are the same, and so is the use of imagination. Already William Whewell saw, over a hundred years ago, that the elemental or generative act in scientific discovery is an idea, the consequences of which can then be tested. Newton's extension of the force pulling the apple to the earth to the force preventing the moon from flying off at a tangent was an idea. Darwin's principle of natural selection was an idea. Mendel's system of segregation and recombination of particulate hereditary factors was an idea.   And this leads straight back to the book under review which is, above all, a notable contribution to the History of Ideas.

I am well aware that I have not answered the Chinese examination paper; I don't know all the answers, and that is why I have preferred to write about the problems and the questions which this book raises.

CHAPTER
10

Genetics and Prehistory

The Rede Lecture delivered before the University of Cambridge on May 27, 1965.

Everyone is interested in how far he can trace a personal connexion backwards in time, and it is an attractive problem to discover who were the earliest recognizable ancestors of the populations of western Europe today. There are plenty of possible ancestors to choose from. The main centres of evolution[1] of land animals were in the large land-masses of the tropical Old World, Asia for the early mammals and probably Africa for Man. Whichever it was, the new products of evolution streamed away in succession from their cradles literally to the ends of the earth, pursued by their more efficient successors, constantly overflowing from the evolutionary cauldrons behind them. Among these ends of the earth (which are more easily recognizable in maps constructed on an equal-area projection), South Africa, South

America, and Malaya, was western Europe, a cul-de-sac further than which no land animal could go without falling into the sea. This is why wave after wave of men came to western Europe and stopped there, piling up race upon race like a thick sandwich. There were primitive forms like Heidelberg and Steinheim Man, followed by Neanderthal Man, followed by the first men of really modern type such as the Cro-Magnon who lived from about 40,000 to 10,000 years ago, and were responsible for the magnificent rock paintings in southern France, Spain, and Portugal. They were followed by Neolithic peoples, agriculturalists and herdsmen, and these by waves of others bringing with them the cultures of the Bronze Age and the Iron Age.

Some years ago, anthropologists noticed a similarity between the skulls of Cro-Magnon Man and some of the inhabitants of southern France at the present time, from which they deduced that these inhabitants were the descendants of Cro-Magnon Man. This view found its way into the textbooks,[2] but it took two things for granted: first, that there was no discontinuity in the habitation by man of the region in question, and secondly, that similarity in skull-shape was a reliable guide to affinity and descent. Neither is free from serious doubt.

Cro-Magnon Man in the Old Stone Age was a hunter whose staple diet was reindeer, an animal adapted to the cold climates that then prevailed under the conditions of the Ice Age. But when the Ice Age came to an end, about 10,000 years ago, and the climate became warmer, two things happened: the reindeer moved away northwards, following up the retreating zone of cold, and the lowlands of Europe became covered with dense forests. Both these changes completely altered the ecological conditions under which men lived. If they stayed where they were, they lacked their principal source of food and their movements were impeded.[3] So far as can be seen, the men moved out and either followed the reindeer northwards or the retreating glaciers of the Alps and the Pyrenees, or they came to the sea coasts and river estuaries, where they eked out a new kind of existence, eating small game, fish and shellfish, of which the kitchen middens strewn from the shores of Portugal to the North Sea are a dismal relic. This was the Mesolithic period, and if there were any men in the centre of France about 5000 B.C. they must have been scared out of their wits, for that was when the chain of volcanoes of the Puys

in Auvergne were last in active eruption.[4]   In any case, when Neolithic
Man arrived from the east the human population of inland regions in
western Europe must have been very sparse, which makes it unlikely
that Cro-Magnon Man left any descendants there to the present day.

As for the shape of the skull, much work and energy have been
devoted to measuring, computing cephalic indices of lengths and
breadths, and comparing skulls of ancient and modern peoples.[5] Not
long ago anthropologists could be seen wandering about in Welsh and
Cotswold villages with callipers in their hands, looking for survivors
of Neolithic peoples. The whole of craniometry had been based on
comparisons between static materials, and when a group of skulls
showed, for instance, a preponderance of long heads, the conclusion
was drawn that the race was pure and that skull-shapes were hereditarily
determined.

The variability of groups of skulls is much greater than was realized.[6]
In British Neolithic skulls, 40 per cent were long-headed with a cephalic
index of 72, but of the remainder some were even longer-headed with
an index of 62, while others were very round-headed with an index
of 85. It now appears certain that round-headedness has been evolved
independently many times in human history, as an effect of paedomorphosis[7] or retention of youthful features, and that it does not
necessarily reflect genetic affinity. In general, country dwellers have
been found to have rounder heads than town dwellers,[8] and inhabitants
of mountainous regions, whatever their race, rounder heads than
dwellers of the plains.[9] In the small Swiss village of Illgau, which
has been, and is, so isolated that intermarriage has been extensive for
centuries,[10] the variation in head shape extends from extreme long-
headedness (index 62) to extreme round-headedness. As this is as
close as anyone could get to a pure community under a constant
environment, it is discouraging to upholders of the purely hereditary
nature of head shape.

Worse is to follow from the results of the application of genetics to
the problem. Measurements have been made on head shapes of related
members of known families studied through three generations.[11]
Variability is high, and some of it seems definitely to be due to
non-hereditary causes. These are numerous and have not yet been
completely worked out, but they include absolute size of the body,
and diet which influences not only teeth but muscles attached to the

skull, both of which have profound effects on the development and shape of the bones.[12] The climate, especially cold and damp, affects the size of the nostrils. In Mongoloids, exposed to extreme cold, reduction in the nasal aperture through which air is breathed in has been accompanied by a deepening of the nasal passage, as a result of which the air is a little more heated by the lining of the nose before it reaches the lungs. This has involved a forward development of the cheek bones, reduction in the salient of the nose, vertical extension of the eye sockets, and reduction of brow ridges. The Mongol face is flattened, which reduces its surface area. This has been called "climatic engineering"[13] of the shape of the skull, and it shows how dangerous it is to regard the latter as an invariably reliable guide to affinity.

Among the descendants of the Maronites who left their native Levant for North America, the cephalic index has gone down[14] from 88 to 79. Japanese born in Hawaii tend to have rounder heads than their parents who were born in Japan.[15] The sugar-loaf shape and flat back of the head characteristic of Dinaric and Armenian peoples may even be a result of obstetric methods and cradling.[16] All this means that the part played by hereditary factors in controlling the shape of the head is complex and obscure,[17] and this is why anthropologists prefer to use a new and different genetic instrument that has come into their hands.

It has been known since the beginning of this century that the human race is divided into four blood groups of the ABO system.[18] During the First World War—and one of its few benefits—it was noticed that in the contingents of the allied armies in Macedonia, drawn from many regions of the world, the percentages in which the four blood groups O, A, B, and AB occurred were different in the different populations. This report was at first received with great scepticism, but it was soon confirmed; and as each blood-group is simply controlled by Mendelian genes, there is here a criterion that can be used to determine affinity not only between persons but between races. In some nations the law accepts blood groups as admissible evidence in paternity suits.

Nobody knows what the functional significance of the blood groups is, but it is known that they play extraordinary and very important parts in characters shown by populations. The different blood groups of the ABO system are differently correlated with longevity, fertility, and liability to cancer of certain organs;[19] they may even affect popular preferences for pronunciations, such as that of the English *th* sound which also appears in the Spanish lisp and the Greek theta.[20] It seems that these are regularly pronounced where the percentage of blood-group gene O exceeds 65, which it does in Iceland, the British Isles, Spain (but not Portugal), Italy (where the Etruscans pronounced *th*), Greece, Crete, and Cyprus. Where the percentage of gene O lies between 65 and 60, it seems that the populations pronounced *th* in the past but ceased to do so, as in Scandinavia and Germany, and the loss can be traced during the Middle Ages progressively from south to north. Populations with less than 60 per cent O seem not to have accepted the pronunciation of *th*.

Although they must be adaptive for some reason, and subject to selection, the percentages in which blood groups are found in endogamous populations can remain constant for at least 1,000 years. Gypsies in Europe have the same distribution pattern as some inhabitants of north-west India, whence they came 1,000 years ago.[21] This is quite different from the European pattern where gypsies live. The Swiss Walsers who emigrated from the Valais in the thirteenth century and colonized Davos, Arosa, Avers, and many other valleys in the Grisons show a blood-group pattern distinctive from that of their neighbours[22] and rather similar to that of the Valaisans who stayed at home, from whom they have been separated for 700 years.[23] German colonies planted in Hungary 500 years ago show the same pattern as Germans in Hamburg today,[24] quite different from that of Hungarians. The further east a population lives or comes from, the higher its percentage of blood-group gene B, which must have originated in the east.

Turning now to the percentages of the ABO genes in western Europe,[25] gene A is found in under 25 per cent of the population in the Basque country, Liguria and the upper valley of the river Po, Corsica, Sardinia, Sicily, Calabria, part of north-west France and of Wales, almost all Ireland, the north of Scotland, and among the Tuareg Berbers of North Africa. Blood-group gene B is found in less than 5 per cent of the population in the Basque country and part of north-west Spain and Portugal and of north-west France. Blood-group gene O exceeds 70 per cent of the population in the Basque country, Liguria, Corsica, Sardinia, parts of north-west France and of Wales, all Ireland and Scotland, and among the Tuaregs.

From this rapid and incomplete survey two facts emerge. The first is the correlation of Mediterranean peoples with low percentages of genes B and A and high percentages of O, shown particularly by populations inhabiting the Basque country and Liguria. The second is the broad blood-group pattern similarity between these peoples and those of north-western Europe in parts of Brittany, Wales, Ireland, and Scotland. It is in the light of these findings that it is possible to set out again in quest of the earliest recognizable ancestors of the present populations of western Europe.

Apart from the enigmatical Cynetes described by Herodotus as living beyond the Celts,[26] history through the writings of classical antiquity relates that the first known inhabitants of western Europe were Ligurians, a people of whom Cato said[27] that they were ignorant liars about whose origins nobody could remember anything. Poseidonios, who travelled in Gaul about 100 B.C., described the Ligurians as wretched, rough, downtrodden people who eked out a miserable existence for themselves by hewing the rocks of their rugged lands.[28] He also told the story of a Ligurian woman who gave birth while working in the fields and immediately continued to work. It is clear from Festus Avienus's description[29] that formerly the territory occupied by Ligurians extended from the Mediterranean to the Atlantic seaboard and the Channel, before they were invaded, subjugated and chased away, first by the Celts and then by the Romans, so that in the end the Ligurians were restricted to the barren, inhospitable, and inaccessible valleys and fastnesses of the southern Alps and the northern Apennines, in Provence, Piedmont, Liguria, and Apuania.[30]

This reduction of the Ligurian lands must have covered a long period of time and must have taken place progressively. Marseilles was founded in Ligurian territory about 600 B.C., and the Celts or Gauls do not seem to have reached the Mediterranean until three centuries later, when they forced their way through between the Ligurians and the Iberians and occupied regions where Hannibal encountered them in 218 B.C. Provence seems to have persisted long in the possession of the Ligurians,[31] who built the marvellous fortresses of Entremont, Saint-Blaise, Glanum, and Roquepertuse before they were finally subdued by Augustus after many bloody wars. The names of their tribes were inscribed on the monument of La Turbie and on the triumphal arch at Susa.

Aristotle described the place where the Rhône runs underground after leaving the Lake of Geneva as in Ligurian territory.[32] Festus Avienus gave the names of the tribes living in the Swiss Valais, Tylangii, Clahilci, Daliterni, and in the Lemenic lands, which are the shores of Lake Leman, all Ligurian names as is also Geneva itself, homonym of Genova in the heart of Liguria.[33] This leads to a consideration of the evidence provided by place-names.

Practically nothing is known of the Ligurian language. The so-called Lepontian inscriptions[34] found in southern Switzerland and near the Italian lakes are already so heavily permeated with Celtic morphological forms,[35] including declension case-endings, that they must be regarded as representing the language of Celtic peoples inhabiting former Ligurian lands and retaining some pre-Indo-European forms, such as the suffix -ikna, Metelikna, daughter of Metellus. The word car, rock, found in Carrara, and the word alb, high pasture, found in Alps, Albula (which is both an alpine pass and the old name of the river Tiber), Albenga on the Riviera, and Alba in the south of France, are Ligurian. A Ligurian remnant has been found in the peculiar pro-nunciation heard in Apuania which the phoneticians call inversion.[36] Instead of gallina they say gadina, and as this phonetic feature is not Indo-European, and as there never were any Celts in Apuania, it must be regarded as a Ligurian relic.

Further progress can be made with the help of place-names. If anyone should be unfamiliar with their possible significance and fascination, he might consider Saragossa and Caesarea Augusta said quickly, or Istanbul and the Doric or Aeolic Greek form eis tan polin, or Shahr-i Sikandari in Afghanistan and Alexander the Great, or Kurkath in Sogdiana and Cyrus and his Cyropolis.[37] Twenty-five centuries is not too long a time for place-names to span.

The Ligurian name for the river Po was "Bodincos,"[38] and the suffix -inca, -inco is recognized as Ligurian, which seemed to like the juxta-position of nasal and guttural sounds, as in -kna. Another valuable source for place-names is the Sententia Minuciorum, a Roman judge-ment on local territorial claims made in 117 B.C., found on an inscription near Genoa.[39] It enumerates many names ending in -asca: Neviasca, Tulelasca, Veraglasca, Vinelasca. Similar names are contained in the Tabula Alimentaria Veleiatium[40] of A.D. 102. These led d'Arbois de Jubainville to suggest that the former extent of Ligurian territories could be traced by place-names ending in -inca, -anca, -asca, -esco and similar forms used as guide "fossils."[41]

In testing the validity of this hypothesis, Corsica is very useful because it was never invaded by Celts, and if non-Latin names are found there they must be non-Indo-European and relics of the Ligurian or Mediterranean stratum of inhabitants. This is supported by Sallust, who in 40 B.C. referred to Corsicans as Ligurians,[42] and Seneca, who said in A.D. 41 that the Corsicans spoke Ligurian.[43] The old name for Elba —Ilva—is that of the Ligurian tribe of the Ilvates.[44] Ptolemy placed the town of Asinkon in Corsica,[45] and even today the island is full of names like Casinca, Cipronasco, Fozzaninco, and Calanca, which means a cleft between steep rocks.[46] It follows that these suffixes may be trusted as Ligurian or Mediterranean, and a faint similarity can be seen between them and some pre-Hellenic names in Greece. The -assa, -asso found, for instance, in Parnassos resemble the Ligurian -asca suffix,[47] and there may be a parallel between the Ligurian -inco and the pre-Hellenic -intho, Corinthos, asaminthos.

Coming now to Liguria, Piedmont, and Lombardy, they are full of names like Cherasco, Gordalasca, Germanasca, Anzasca, which can be counted in hundreds. They decrease in number eastwards, and none is found east of the Adige. It is possible that they include the name of the Val Camonica, where hundreds of rock drawings have been found[48] comparable with the thousands near Mont Bégo in Liguria, showing agricultural scenes.[49] In southern Switzerland these names are very numerous, including Ascona, Bignasco, Biasca, Giubiasco, Bondasca, Altanca, Val Calanca. In Roman times Vevey was Viviscus,[50] and the military station near Bienne was Petinesca. The old name for the Rhône itself, Rhotanos, is identical with the name applied by Ptolemy to the river Tavignano in Corsica.[51]

Passing into Provence, the mute e which in French has taken the place of the vowel in non-accentuated terminal syllables, and which sometimes vanishes altogether, does not hide the Ligurian origin of Manosque, Vénasque, Lambesc, Albiosc, Sénanque, Lémenc. The word calanque, a cleft between rocks giving access to the sea, has passed into current vocabulary all along the Riviera. Where the accent on the last syllable was preserved, as in Tarascon, or Mâcon which Julius Caesar called "Matisco,"[52] the Ligurian origin is clear. In many cases the modern form hides its origin,[53] but medieval manuscripts easily reveal it: Aubignan was Albinosco, Gap was Vapincum, Veynes was Davincum, the river Séveraisse was Severiasca. The Mont Lassois near Châtillon-sur-Seine, where the treasure of Vix was found, was Latisco.[54] The adjectives Monégasque, Mentonasque, Turbiasque, Tendasque, like the Italian Comasco and Bergamasco, betray their Ligurian origin.[55]

These place-name fossils in France decrease in number northwards but can be traced up to the latitude of Paris. As they represent relics of a defeated and annihilated population, they mostly refer to obscure and retired places, and there is no danger of exaggerating their number, as the majority must have been forgotten and lost. To the west of the Rhône these fossil names are also found, as far as Tarascon and Huesca in the Pyrenees, but this is the country of the Basques whose name, Vascuence, the Vascones vanquished by Pompey, the Gascons, whose country, Biscaya, and whose language, Euskarian, all contain the -asca form. This demonstration would have delighted Leibniz, who in 1701 specifically recommended the study of Basque place-names to solve the problem of their origin.[56] It also leads to the question that Élisée Reclus put to himself,[57] whether the Ligurians were related to the Basques.

The Basques today live in seven provinces, four in Spain—Alava, Biscaya, Guipuzcoa and Navarre—and three in France—Basse-Navarre, Labourd, and Soule. As a people they are short with dark eyes and hair and pointed chins, and are possessed of a phenomenal muscular strength and powers of resistance. Their traditions and customs are peculiar to them, and their language has nothing in common, either in basic vocabulary or in syntax, with any Indo-European language. Basque is agglutinative, has passive verbs and preserves traces of a vicesimal numerical system. The words used for cutting instruments such as a knife (*aizto*), a hatchet (*aizkora*), a pickax (*aitzur*), a curved blade (*aihotz*) are all compounded of the word *aitz,* meaning a flint implement.[58] In this respect the etymology of these Basque words is Neolithic.

The Basque territory was formerly much more extensive than it is today. The town of Auch in France was originally called Elimberris, and Granada was Illiberis;[59] Bigorre in France corresponds to Begerra in Old Spain. Inscriptions on lead of the sixth century B.C. found at Cigarralejo in Murcia and at Alicante show analogies with Basque.[60] It has been held that the Iberian language was a form of primitive Basque,[61] which agrees with Strabo's statement that the inhabitants of Aquitaine resembled the Iberians in appearance and in language.[62]

The affinity between Ligurians and Basques is thereby widened into that of the western Mediterranean peoples. Iberians and Ligurians, according to Strabo,[63] and Corsicans, according to Diodorus,[64] practised couvade. Tuledo[65] in Liguria matches Toledo in Spain.

This gives a sharpened meaning to a well-known statement by Caesar, that all Gaul was divided into three parts, the inhabitants of which differed in customs, laws, and languages.[66] North of the Seine-Marne line were Belgi, germanized Celts; between the Seine-Marne and the Garonne, true Celts or Gauls; south of the Garonne the Aquitani or Basque-Iberians, among whom archaeologists have shown that the Gauls had not penetrated by Roman times.[67] All the inhabitants of Gaul were therefore not Gauls.

In this way a case can be made for a general affinity between Ligurians, Basques, and Iberians, but a proof can be supplied by the study of the Rhesus blood groups.[68] The highest percentages of the Rhesus-negative gene in the world are found in the populations of Spanish Basques (65), French Basques (59), and Berbers (55), and then come populations near Genoa in Liguria, Brescia and Bergamo in the Po valley (46). A gradient of decreasing values of the Rhesus-negative gene can be seen at increasing distances from the Pyrenees;[69] at Montpellier it is 43, in Paris 41, and in Britain the average is 39. Reclus's surmise that the Basques were related to the Ligurians can therefore be accepted as correct. It follows that the Ligurian language, like the Basque, was non-Indo-European, and that the Basque language, like the Ligurian, is pre-Indo-European. The Basques therefore represent the purest sample left of the pre-Indo-European populations of western Europe before the waves of Indo-European Celts overran the land.

The Rhesus blood groups supply a further piece of information. In western Europe generally, apart from the Basque country, a frequency of 40 per cent of the Rhesus-negative gene in the population means that about 15 per cent of individuals are Rhesus-negative and 85 per cent Rhesus-positive, because the Rhesus-negative gene is recessive and is carried as such by about 25 per cent of the people, who do not show it because they have one Rhesus-positive gene to mask its effects. This situation, however, is genetically unstable. When a Rhesus-negative woman bears a child by a Rhesus-positive man, his gene, being dominant, appears and is active in their child. While it is still in the womb, its Rhesus-positive antigens may get through the placental membrane and stimulate the Rhesus-negative mother to produce anti-bodies which may return across the placental membrane and cause haemolytic disease of the newborn in an appreciable number of cases. This is an example of the imperfection of adaptation, for man's ancestors have been viviparous for at least two hundred million years, but this mode of reproduction has not yet become adapted to the immuno-logical defence mechanisms of the body.[70]   At every death from haemolytic disease one Rhesus-positive gene and one Rhesus-negative gene are lost, and as the Rhesus-positive genes in the population of west-ern Europe are the more numerous, the relative number of Rhesus-negative genes will decrease to some level where it will be in balance with other factors affecting the natural selection of this character. Western European man is in a condition known to biologists as tran-sient polymorphism for the Rhesus genes.[71]

Haemolytic disease would not, as it were, be built into a population which was either wholly Rhesus-positive or wholly Rhesus-negative, and the condition now found in western Europe can only have been due to the superimposition of a Rhesus-positive population of invaders over a pre-existing Rhesus-negative population. The part of the latter was evi-dently played by the peoples of the Mediterranean race, represented by Ligurians and Basques, while the part of the former must have been played by the Indo-European Celtic invaders. The genetics of blood groups in this way allows a glimpse to be caught of an important event in European prehistory, the superimposition of one race over another, and as the Neolithic Age was the heyday of the Mediterranean race, the biological picture presented by genetics is that of the transition from the Neolithic to the Bronze Age.

The chronology of this transition is difficult to determine, but esti-mates have been made based on two lines of research, archaeology and linguistics. There is now incontrovertible evidence that two Indo-European languages, Hittite and Greek, were fully formed by the middle of the second millennium b.c., and it is not extravagant to suppose that they and the other Indo-European languages, including the Celtic, were differentiated before that millennium.[72] This agrees with the conclusion that the Indo-European community must be placed well back in the third millennium.[73] In an attempt to find a statistical method of estimating the rate of change in the basic vocabulary of languages, it has been calculated that about 20 per cent of this vocabulary is changed in one thousand years,[74] and therefore where languages have diverged the time elapsed since such divergence can be estimated. The method admittedly involves some assumptions and is still crude, but its results are in general agreement with these conclusions. The Celtic languages would have been brought westwards, together with the Rhesus-positive gene, some 4,000 years ago. This would allow some 150 generations during which segregation and recombination of the Rhesus genes have taken place to give rise to the situation that prevails today in western Europe.

If the Mediterranean race occupied Gaul as far as the Atlantic and Channel shores, it is natural to inquire whether that race also occupied Britain. It is generally admitted that the Neolithic Windmill Hill people, who came to Britain in the third millennium, were of Mediterranean origin, and Tacitus made no bones about calling the Silures, primitive inhabitants of Wales, Iberians.[75] Hibernia contains the form *iber* unaltered. It was among such people that the megalithic "movement," doubtless brought from the Mediterranean by "missionaries," became established and led to the building of monuments in Brittany, Cornwall, the Isles of Scilly, Ireland, Wales, and Scotland. In some cases it is possible to track down the Mediterranean regions of origin of the styles of these megalithic monuments.[76] The Clyde-Carlingford series have their prototypes in the south of France; the Severn-Cotswold series have theirs near the mouth of the Loire. The passagegraves of Ireland follow the Iberian style, while the covered galleries of the Isles of Scilly, the Isle of Man, and Scotland reflect Sardinian and Pyrenean models.

Archaeology therefore supplies evidence of a connexion between western Britain and the Mediterranean in Neolithic times, and this provides an answer to a question often asked and wrongly answered. In the west of Brittany, Cornwall, Ireland, Wales, and Scotland are found people with dark eyes and jet-black hair who have, completely erroneously, been spoken of as "Celtic."[77] On the contrary, the Celts had fair or fiery red hair and blue eyes, as Roman writers well knew. Nor can the Spaniards of the Armada be invoked. The dark hair and eyes of people in these regions of Britain are due to dominant genes which they have inherited from their original Mediterranean race ancestors. They are concentrated in the western extremities of the country for the

same reason that the Celts became concentrated there, having been
driven westwards by successive waves of later invaders.

Their hair and eyes are not the only links that they show with a
remote past. Another is the ceremony of the "mock-mayors" which
was carried out up till recently in Cornwall.[78] After his election the
"mayor" was treated with respect which soon gave way to insult and
violence when he was carted about and finally thrown with ignominy
on a manure heap, amid scenes of increasing drunkenness and dis-
order. This was the vestige of an annual feast of licence or saturnalia,
accorded to a subjugated population by its new masters. The latter
were the warrior invaders of the Bronze Age, the former the Neolithic
Mediterranean peoples.

Place-names in Britain also show Mediterranean links. To explain
the name of London by invoking an hypothetical and unknown Celtic
person called Londinos is pure invention. *Lond-* is a Mediterranean
form[79] found in Londobris, the name given by Ptolemy to the Ber-
lengas Islands.[80] Kent Cantium is to be compared with Basque *cantal,*
a stone, or Cantabria in the Basque country. Ptolemy's name for Canterbury,[81] "Darouernon," contains the Mediterranean pre-Indo-European
form *-ern.* Still in Kent, Richborough is Ptolemy's "Routoupiae,"
Lucan's[82] "Rutupina," the Venerable Bede's[83] "Portus Rutubi," which
may be compared with "Rutuba," the ancient name[84] for the river Roia
that runs into the Mediterranean at Bordighera in the heart of Liguria.
The rivers Fal, Fowey, and Coffer[85] in Cornwall are non-Indo-European,
as are Teviot and Ouse. Thames and Tamar are to be compared with
Tamarus in Samnium, Tamara in Iberia, and Damurias in Sicily.[86]
Finally, Albion with the high cliffs of Dover, and Albany with the
mountains of Scotland, contain the Ligurian form *alb.* So the oldest
identifiable ancestors of present populations in western Europe turn out
to be the Neolithic Mediterranean peoples, from whom at least some
genes have been inherited and some customs and names transmitted.

The little that is known about the Picts gives a glimpse of the pre-
Indo-European inhabitants of Scotland.[87] That their language was non-
Indo-European can be deduced from the fact that when Columba came
from Ireland to Scotland, where the Celtic language was already well
established by the *Scoti,* he needed an interpreter to speak to the
Picts.[88] The place-names Caledonia and Graupius are non-Indo-European, as are a dozen names of rivers and half a dozen tribes mentioned

by Ptolemy. Schiehallion, Rohallion, Dunkeld, and the river-names Isla, Affric, Liver and Nevis are non-Indo-European. The same conclusion emerges from the inscriptions in ogham characters such as Edarnon (stones of Scoonie and Brodie), Idarnoin (Fordoun and Lunnasting), Irataddoarens (Brandsbutt), and many others. Many of the names of kings in the Pictish Chronicle are very outlandish, such as Bliesblituth, Usconbuts and Canatulachama. Finally, there is an item of information given by Bede which he himself seems not fully to have understood. This was the mode of succession of Pictish kings.[89]

A Pictish king was not succeeded by his son even if he had one, but by his mother's next male relative who might be a brother or a nephew of the previous king. This is the matrilinear system, which was well shown in the Mediterranean by the Etruscans and the kings of Rome,[90] many of whom were Etruscan and non-Indo-European. Not one was succeeded by his son; most were succeeded by their son-in-law or by their mother's grandson. There are other traces of matrilinear succession in Britain, among the Irish Tuatha dè Danann and in the Welsh poem *Hanes Taliesin*.[91] It seems to have been general in the Mediterranean in Neolithic times. The Lemta Tuaregs still preserve it, and among the Basques today lawyers pay particular attention to property inherited from the mother.

Socially the matrilinear system may derive from a stage when people were polyandrous, as it has been suggested that the early peoples of North Britain were. Until the physiological fact of paternity was recognized, the maternal was the only possible line of descent that anybody could have. Biologically the matrilinear system allows exogamy to take place. The daughter of the Ligurian chief who received the Phocean Greek leader Euxenos at Marseilles herself chose him as her husband, and several of the Pictish kings appear to have borne Celtic names.[92]

Matrilinear succession is a stage in the evolution of social structure from the matriarchal state when the queen reigned as the incarnation of the Mother-Goddess, who bore various names: Isis in Egypt, Ishtar in Babylonia, Cybele in Asia Minor, Hera in pre-Hellenic Greece. In Basque folklore she is still Maia. She was often represented in triple form with mystical significance and was frequently related to the moon, a heavenly body strongly associated with femaleness among Mediterranean peoples. It would be interesting to know if the three Maries of Provence, who are also known as les Saintes-Maries-de-la-Mer in the Camargue, represent a christianized survival of the Mother-Goddess in her triple form.

The Mother-Goddess was already represented in statuary form in the Old Stone Age with its "venuses," and it is known that she was worshipped in Britain in Neolithic times by the discovery of a figurine in a flint-mine.[93]

The association between the moon and female deities is connected with the age-old belief that menstrual periods are controlled by the moon. The synodic period of a lunation is 29 days, 12 hours, 44 minutes, subject to variation because of the eccentricity of the moon's orbit. The period of menstruation varies between 21 and 37 days, with an average value in Britain of 28.7 days. This value has, however, no significance, for the real value varies from one period to another in the same subject and decreases with age. There is no basis for attributing to the moon any part whatever in the physiological cause of a process that involves the liberation of hormones alternately from the pituitary gland and the ovary, resulting in the cybernetic control of the process.[94] The average periods of moon and women are, however, sufficiently similar to have given rise to a belief in their correlation, especially before the year 1656 when Christiaan Huygens, for the first time in the history of the world, made it possible by means of the pendulum clock to reckon time for prolonged periods more accurately than to the nearest half day. The belief must have played an important part in attributing supernatural and astronomical significance to female processes and therefore to the matriarchal principle.

Under the matriarchal system the king wielded his power only in virtue of his association with the queen, and at first for only a limited period, after which he was killed as a sacrifice as part of a fertility rite. Later a scapegoat was substituted for him. A trace of this practice is still found in the ceremony of "crying the neck," carried out until recently in Provence and apparently still preserved in Cornwall.[95] When the last sheaf of wheat is cut, it is decked out with ribbons which make it into a doll, a very rough representation of the corn-goddess. The reapers then recite a litany the meaning of which has long since been forgotten, but which was intended to propitiate the corn spirit in the corn-goddess for the damage done by the sickle, and to entreat fertility in the following year. This is a typical Neolithic sentiment, when for the first time in man's existence he was provided by agriculture with an assured food-supply instead of living like a hunter from hand to mouth.

The matriarchal and matrilinear systems were followed by the patrilinear and patriarchal which were practised by Indo-European peoples. This transition, which accompanied the passage from an agricultural civilization associated with matrilinear customs to a stock-raising system of herdsmen associated with patriarchal customs,[96] is another aspect of the change from the Neolithic to the Bronze Age. This change also affected religious beliefs and architecture. The earliest megalithic monuments built by Neolithic peoples were chambers, either hollowed out in rock or covered with stones and earth, evoking the mystery of darkness as in night, associated with the moon, and as in the womb.[97] Later, in the Bronze Age, stone monuments, such as those at Carnac, Stonehenge, or Avebury, were temples associated with the sun and the sky, male principles, reflecting the replacement of the female deities of the pre-Indo-European peoples by the male sky god and thunder god of the Indo-Europeans.

Professor Robert Graves has suggested that the battle of the sexes among gods and men can be followed in the evolution of the Greek myths.[98] When the Indo-European Achaeans penetrated into Greece, they found peoples who worshipped Hera, Athene, Demeter and other deities, to whom were then joined Zeus, Poseidon, and Hades, Hellenic representatives of the Indo-European gods Mithra, Indra, and Varuna. In this mixed pantheon, Zeus soon arrogated to himself powers that made him insufferable to his colleagues, who revolted against him, led by Hera, and almost triumphed. But Zeus won in the end, and his revenge was terrible. He hung Hera up to the sky by golden bracelets on each arm and tied an anvil to each of her ankles. This myth may reflect a revolt by the pre-Hellenic inhabitants against their new masters, put down with savage repression, as the Helots regularly were by the Spartans. The final blow to the original matrilinear system of the old population was reflected in the mythical birth of Athene from the brow of Zeus, without any maternal participation. This also consecrated the male monopoly of wisdom. The scene was then set for male predominance, which was exerted wherever the Indo-Europeans became established, although there were some exceptions and delays, as in the case of the sixth century B.C. princess of Vix whose fantastically beautiful tomb furniture has been excavated near Châtillon-sur-Seine.[99] There were also Cartimandua, queen of the Brigantes, and Boadicea, queen of the Iceni, concerning whom Tacitus went out of his way to relate the fact that Britons were wont to fight under the orders of women, as if it were something extraordinary.[100]

This excursion through four millennia and from the Mediterranean to John o'Groats leads to the conclusion that the oldest links with the past that living populations in western Europe can claim are shown by genes, place-names, and customs, with Neolithic Mediterranean peoples, particularly in the so-called Celtic lands, in Liguria and Provence, and in the Basque country. These were the regions where a curious new movement arose in the Dark Ages. In the midst of the savagery and violence of the feudal system, a feeling of tenderness and chivalry appeared in legends, poems, and stories. There had been nothing quite like it in classical antiquity, Anglo-Saxon literature, Norse sagas, the Nibelungenlied, or the *chansons de geste,* violent and gross military epics. The new love-poetry included the legends of Tristan and Iseult and of King Arthur and his Knights of the Round Table, who devoted themselves to the succour of damsels in distress. These legends concerned Wales, Ireland, and Cornwall, and collectively they became known as *matière de Bretagne.* William of Aquitaine launched the fashion of courtesy, which was taken up by the troubadours of Provence, where courts of love were set up. Eleanor of Aquitaine brought the movement to the north of France and, in the words of Lanson and Tuffrau,[101] "La femme, récemment encore servante méprisée de l'homme, se trouve placée au-dessus de lui, adorée, servie, obéie" ("Woman, recently still the despised servant of man, finds herself placed above him, adored, served, obeyed"). Was it pure accident that the regions involved in this movement are those where genes, place-names, and customs indicate links with the Neolithic matrilinear peoples?

However that may be, there was, on the practical side, still work for the English suffragette Mrs. Pankhurst to do. There is a story told of her which, for all its absurdity, serves to show an aspect of the difference between Neolithic and modern times. On one of the many occasions when she was arrested and placed in a cell, she heard one of her companions in the next cell sobbing and whimpering, so she shouted through her door, "Stop it, you should pray to God, and She will help you." This would not have sounded funny to Neolithic ears, but then they would not have arrested Mrs. Pankhurst.

I am aware that I have attempted to sketch a picture with a very broad brush on a very large canvas, and that nearly everything that I have said may be controverted. But what I have been principally concerned to do was to show how natural science—in this case genetics, anatomy, and physiology—can be applied to problems of history and prehistory. Elsewhere[102] I have endeavoured to do this with the origin of the Etruscans, Hannibal's pass, the identification of Diodorus's *Iktin* with St. Michael's Mount, and Gibbon's malady, and there are countless more problems where this could be done. Our unique cultural heritage is so rich that it has become split into many streams, and if only some of them could be knitted together again, knowledge and pleasure would be greatly enriched.

CHAPTER
11

Atlantis: The Historical and Scientific Interpretation of an Event

It would be difficult to find a classical subject more heavily charged with emotive overtones and beguiling attractions of mysticism than that conjured up by the word "Atlantis." It calls up visions of a great lost paradise, a wonderful vanished civilization sunk beneath "the vasty deep" of the western ocean, where the Isles of the Blessed were supposed to be, to which some have looked for the origin of ideals and customs which they find it difficult to attribute to the violent barbarians, wave after wave of which have come from the East to pile themselves up in western Europe. Sentimental attraction to what is sometimes called "Celtic Twilight," and resistance to the fact, quite undeniable, that the Celts came from the East, die hard. Furthermore, the theosophists have fastened on Atlantis as the cradle of their alleged race of superior civilization, endowed with second sight and occult powers over the forces of nature, supposedly descended from the inhabitants of a vanished continent in the Indian Ocean, "Lemuria," which certainly never existed. There are tactical advantages in situating the scenes of unverifiable events in inaccessible places. Words sometimes have the power of guiding thoughts instead of being their means of expression, and the name "Atlantis" has played a large part in colouring and distorting views on the interpretation of a fascinating story that goes back 3,500 years to describe a tragic event.

The *Oxford Companion to English Literature* defines Atlantis as "a fabulous island in the ocean west of the Pillars of Hercules, a beautiful and prosperous country, the seat of an empire which dominated part of Europe and Africa. But owing to the impiety of its inhabitants, it was swallowed up by the sea." *Larousse Classique* says of Atlantis that it was "a continent which, according to the ancients and some geologists, would have covered part of the Atlantic Ocean." The *Enciclopedia Italiana* labels Atlantis as the subject of a fable, and Pauly-Wissowa's *Real-Lexicon* calls it a myth. With this general background in current works of reference, it is not surprising that there are to be found many persons, including distinguished scholars, historians, and archaeologists, who do not consider the story of Atlantis to be anything more than a fairy tale, a work of that imagination which was so fertile in the minds of the classical Greeks in their myths, legends, and poems. This is in spite of, or even perhaps because of, the distinguished parenthood of the story, for its author was none other than Plato, who recounted it in two of his *Dialogues*. Scholarship, archaeology, and a newcomer in their company, natural science, have combined in recent years to show that the story of Atlantis, for all its apparently fictional nature, is not a figment of Plato's imagination, but contains the essential ingredients of the account of an historic event which can now be situated in time and in place.

The Story of Atlantis

All textual knowledge of Atlantis stems from Plato's *Timaeus* and *Critias,* dialogues which form a sequel to the *Republic* and provide the author with the opportunity to give an exposition of his views on the origin and system of the universe. The speakers include Timaeus, a

Pythagorean philosopher; Critias, an historical figure among Athenian politicians and leader of the Thirty Tyrants; and Socrates. Written about 375 B.C., the dialogues are placed about 410 B.C. when Socrates was still alive. The story of Atlantis, as an episode in the history of Greece, is related by Critias, whose great-grandfather Dropides learnt it from his cousin Solon, the law-giver of Athens. Dropides told it to his son Critias the Elder, from whom Critias heard it himself. As Solon, Critias, and Plato himself were all related, the story takes on the form of a family tradition.

In the *Timaeus,* after Socrates has recapitulated some of the arguments of the *Republic,* Critias speaks and recounts what Solon had said to his grandfather. The story starts by referring to the city of Sais in the delta of the Nile in Egypt, which Solon visited about 594 B.C., and where he asked the priests questions about their ancient history. Solon had told them the legend of Deucalion's Flood which was supposed to have devastated Greece, and had given the genealogy of Deucalion's and Pyrrha's descendants, the Greeks, whereupon an old Saitic priest protested that the Greeks knew nothing of their ancient history, because the floods that devastated their country swept all the educated town-dwellers into the sea, leaving as only survivors the mountain-dwellers, herdsmen and shepherds, who were uncultured and unable to make or preserve written records. In Egypt, on the contrary, where no rain falls and the rise in the waters of the Nile is well known, every event of importance that occurred in Egypt or in other countries was recorded and preserved in the temples.

Among these events, the priest told Solon, was the great service which the men of Athens had rendered to mankind, nine thousand years before, when by their valour they prevented the State of Atlantis from conquering and enslaving Europe and Asia. Atlantis was a great island, as big as Libya and Asia, situated in the ocean beyond the Pillars of Hercules, from which it was possible to cross to other islands and to the continents. It was a confederation of very rich and powerful princes who held sway over many islands and even over parts of continents. They already ruled over Libya as far as Egypt, and over Europe as far as Tuscany, when they made a bid for mastery of the world by attacking Egypt and Greece. With great gallantry, the Athenians defeated them; but then there occurred natural calamities, earthquakes and floods. Attica was visited by a devastating flood that killed countless people; an Athenian army was swallowed up by an earthquake and buried under the earth, and the island of Atlantis disappeared beneath the sea, leaving where it had been mud flats which impeded shipping.

The remainder of the *Timaeus* is concerned with discussion on the creation of the universe, gods, men, the origin of sensations and of diseases, the soul, and what happens after death. The story of Atlantis is taken up in greater detail in the *Critias,* where it is again Critias who speaks. After repeating that nine thousand years before Solon's visit to Sais the leaders of Atlantis attacked the Greeks who were led by the Athenians, and that Atlantis sank beneath the sea as a result of earthquakes, which had given rise to banks of mud that impeded shipping on the way from Egypt to the ocean, Critias went into detail about Atlantis itself before the disaster.

Just as Hephaistos and Athene were the tutelary gods of Athens, Atlantis was the domain of Poseidon, the Earth-shaker. In one place that redoubtable god had established the descendants of a race which he had himself begotten. On a central island, around a low hill or acropolis, three circular concentric canals surrounded by walls had been built, connected with the sea by other canals, and crossed by bridges. The acropolis was therefore impregnable. It had two springs of water, one hot and the other cold. Control of the State of Atlantis was divided between ten sons under the eldest, whose name was Atlas.

The land was extremely rich and prosperous, partly because of trade and products imported from other countries, and partly from its own natural wealth. This included metals, of which those in use were gold, silver, copper, and tin (no iron); forests that provided abundant timber (essential for boat-building); cultivated plants such as cereals, fruit, vegetables, and plants that provided liquids (i.e., oils) and scents; tame and wild animals, including elephants.

On the acropolis was a royal palace in which was a temple dedicated to Poseidon, to whom sacrifices were brought every year. The hot and cold springs supplied water for baths for the princes, citizens, and women. There was a racecourse for horses, the shipyards were well-equipped, and the ships numerous and well-found.

The country also contained a flat rectangular plain, the sides of which measured 3,000 stadia in length by 2,000 stadia in width, open to the sea on the south but surrounded on the other sides by mountains which protected the plain from the north winds. The timber from the mountains and the produce from the plain, which gave two crops a year, were conveyed to the city in ships. The armed forces included ten thousand chariots, with charioteers, riders, and hoplites; also slingers, javelin-throwers, and sailors manning 1,200 ships.

The laws of the State of Atlantis had been laid down by Poseidon and were inscribed on tablets of brass in the central temple, where the ten princes gathered at stated intervals, alternately every fifth and every sixth year, to conduct affairs of state and to sit in judgement. In the precincts of the temple bulls were kept, and the princes hunted them with staves and nooses but without using any metallic weapons. When caught, the bulls were killed so that their blood flowed over the inscription of the law, which the princes then swore to observe, with complicated ceremonial.

Such were the essential features of the story of Atlantis. Among Plato's contemporaries or near-contemporaries, Aristotle (to judge from Strabo's writings) considered it to be imaginary, Crator held it to be true, while Poseidonios of Apamaea considered that it was based on historical fact. Strabo reported Poseidonios as saying that Plato's story of Atlantis might well not be fictional. Among modern writers, one editor of Plato's works, R. G. Bury, labelled it as "a fine piece of literary fiction," while another, Benjamin Jowett, considered that Plato had invented the whole story, including Solon's visit to Egypt. This seems to be excessive scepticism, for Plutarch described Solon's visit to Egypt, which probably took place soon after 600 B.C., and he even gave the name of the most learned priest of Sais, Sonchis, with whom Solon discussed history. Herodotus talked with the assistant treasurer at Sais in his day, and there was nothing improbable in an Athenian Greek's visiting the friendly Egyptians at the beginning of the sixth century B.C.

At the same time, it must be obvious that there are details in the story of Atlantis, particularly as regards time, dimensions, and geographical location, which, if taken literally as they stand, are, for one reason or another, unacceptable. This has led to the most extraordinary hypotheses having been advanced to overcome one or other of these difficulties, only at the expense of falling still deeper into absurdity. This is the chief reason why the whole subject has fallen into discredit and has been brought into disrepute as "history," by the unbridled fancy of all too many amateur puzzle-solvers, whose knowledge and judgement have been inversely proportional to their enthusiasm and effrontery. As early as 1841, Thomas Henri Martin enumerated the various conjectures that had by then tried to place Atlantis in Africa, America, Australasia, Spitzbergen, Sweden, Sardinia, Palestine, Attica, Persia, and Ceylon. To these may be added Heligoland, Nigeria, the region of France where the Cro-Magnon people once lived, an island off the mouth of the river Guadalquivir in Spain serving as an emporium of Tarshish such as Gades, the modern Cadiz, the sebkah of Melah in Tunisia near Gabes, and even the problematical Homeric island of the Phaeacians which Ernle Bradford, with considerable probability, has placed at Corfu. *Ignotum per ignotius.* No useful purpose would be served by perpetuating the names of the authors of such extravagances.

Until fairly recently, the habit was widespread of comparing the accuracy and dependability of the works of ancient authors very unfavourably with those of their modern successors who claimed to be so much better informed. Scorn was poured on Livy's description of the use of fire and vinegar to split rocks, a method which is nevertheless well attested and has recently been repeated experimentally; and on Polybius's assertion that at the battle of Raphia the African elephants were no match for the Indian, a statement now recognized as perfectly correct, because the African elephants in question were not of the type of the great bush elephant of central Africa, but the small forest variety from north Africa. As Pierre Armandi remarked, recent travellers and naturalists have more than once vindicated the ancient writers against the scepticism that modern critics have shown towards their writings, and have confirmed the basic accuracy of descriptions on which doubt had been thrown.

The various elements of the story of Atlantis as told by Plato, and the different interpretations placed on it by recent commentators, will be considered in detail below, where it will be shown, first, that Atlantis cannot have been situated in the Atlantic Ocean, or anywhere else other than in the Mediterranean; second, that the State of Atlantis as described by Plato is an astonishingly accurate description of the Minoan empire of Crete, could not apply to anywhere else and could not have been invented by Plato or any other Greek of the fifth century B.C.; and third, that the cataclysmic eruption of the volcano of Santorin, in the Aegean Sea, north of Crete, now accurately dated to the fifteenth century B.C., can be identified with the disaster that overtook the State of Atlantis.

Atlantis Was Not in the Atlantic Ocean

During the nineteenth century some naturalists, attempting to explain similarities between a few species of plants and animals on either side of an ocean, imagined that the continents now separated by that ocean were originally joined by land which had since become submerged. This was how Edward Forbes was led to propose that there had once been a continent of Atlantis between Europe and North America, to explain how a few species had crossed from one continent to the other, dry-shod. He and those who followed him, in their enthusiasm, completely overlooked the fact that such a land connexion, had it ever existed, must have served as a bridge for infinitely more species than the miserable few that it was called into existence to explain. Land-bridges between existing continents, thrown across ocean basins, make the problem of the geographical distribution of plants and animals completely unintelligible, because the differences between the floras and faunas of the continents are so much greater than the similarities. Darwin was well aware of this, and he showed that the distribution of organisms was satisfactorily explained by migration across even wide stretches of water. Still more damning was the evidence which Darwin brought to bear from geology to show that the floors of oceans had never been continents or dry land. The islands with which oceans are dotted are of volcanic or coralline origin, and quite different from what they would be if they were the projecting unsubmerged tops of mountain ranges of submerged continents.

During the passage of geological time, there have been minor oscillations of the levels of land and sea on the continents and the continental shelf which extends a short distance away from the continents. The melting of the ice cap of Antarctica since the last Ice Age has resulted in the raising of the level of the sea by some six inches a century, and this has been responsible for the submergence of small tracts of land, such as the submerged forest in Mount's Bay off Penzance. The Arthurian legend of the Land of Lyonesse, whose 140 parish churches were said to have been lost beneath the waves, may vaguely, but quite unjustifiably, have been associated with this event; it certainly did not connect Land's End with the Isles of Scilly, which have been separated for a space of time far longer than that since which churches have existed, besides which, it is not at all clear whether the legend of Lyonesse is Cornish or Breton.

That there can be no question of any continent's having been lost beneath the Atlantic Ocean is confirmed by evidence derived from a number of recent lines of research in natural science, relating to what is called the Mohorovicic discontinuity. Taking first the results of seismology, the scientific study of earthquake shocks, it is found that the speed at which primary shock-waves travel through the continental crust after an earthquake is about 5 kilometres a second near the surface, but jumps abruptly to 8 kilometres a second at a depth of about 40 kilometres beneath the surface, the depth at which the Mohorovicic discontinuity is estimated to lie beneath the continents. This difference in speed of transmission of shock-waves represents a difference in the material of which the earth is composed at that depth. Beneath the oceans, on the other hand, the Mohorovicic discontinuity is only 10 kilometres beneath the level of the sea, which shows that there is a structural and material difference between continents and ocean floors.

These results are concordant with those obtained from the measurement of the force of gravity on continents and in oceans. This force varies with the mass of the attracting bodies, and in oceans it invariably shows higher values than on continents. The material of which the ocean bed is formed is denser than that of the continental crust, which shows that the former is not simply a portion of the latter covered by the sea. Continents are composed of granites, gneisses, and sedimentary rocks with an average specific gravity of 2.7, whereas the ocean beds are composed of basalts and even heavier rocks with an average specific gravity of 3.2. They are as different as cheese from chalk, and ocean floors have never been the surfaces of continents.

Running down the middle of the Atlantic Ocean is a submarine ridge, the Mid-Atlantic Ridge, which emerges above the surface of the sea at Saint Paul's Rocks. On examination, the material of which these are composed has been found to conform not to the nature of the constituents of the continental crusts, but to the mantle layer underlying the Mohorovicic discontinuity, here compressed, metamorphosed, folded, and brought up to the surface. It follows that no large area of land, such as Atlantis was supposed to be, can ever have been situated in the

Atlantic Ocean. Recent research has provided evidence in favour of the possibility that continents once drifted over ocean beds; but as this can only have happened hundreds of millions of years ago, it has no bearing whatever on events supposed to have taken place since the evolution of man.

The scientific evidence on which these conclusions are based admits of no argument. It is interesting to find, as will be seen, that a critical analysis of Plato's text reveals features which show that the relegation of the land of Atlantis to somewhere in the Atlantic Ocean was, probably, not the original story, but an interpretation introduced to try to make sense of the alleged dimensions of the land, which made it difficult to accommodate it inside the Mediterranean.

Atlantis Was in the Mediterranean

The attentive reader will already have become aware that there is one technical point in Plato's story of Atlantis that does not make sense and cannot be correct. This is the figure 9,000 attributed to the number of years before Solon's visit to Egypt, when the State of Atlantis was said to have been in the condition described. This condition is that of a state in the Bronze Age. Writing had been invented, as the inscription of the law on metal tablets shows. The metals used were gold, silver, copper, tin, and the alloy brass, none of which were available to men before the Bronze Age. A notable absentee from the list of metals is iron, which was not used before the Iron Age. The date-bracket for the Bronze Age may be taken to be after 2500 B.C. and before 1000 B.C. As Solon's visit to Egypt may be dated about 600 B.C., a date of 9600 B.C. is quite impossible for a culture such as that described for Atlantis. Furthermore, at such a remote date even Egypt, for all its very old civilization, would then have been still in the Stone Age, and in no condition to make records or keep them in temples.

In order to facilitate the subsequent treatment of this problem, this is the place in which to introduce the hypothesis put forward by Angelos Galanopoulos, which makes this discrepancy, and another shortly to be discussed, capable of simple explanation. The hypothesis is that in the translation or transcription of what the Egyptian priest told Solon into the Greek that Solon spoke or wrote, a mistake was made of substituting thousands for hundreds. Such a mistake would have been easier to make than the equivalent modern mistake of adding an extra unwanted naught to a figure, because neither the Egyption nor the Greek figures were based on a decimal system of notation, and did not include naughts. The Egyptian symbol of one hundred was like a picture of a coiled rope; the symbol for one thousand was based on a representation of a lotus flower. The symbols were repeated the number of times required on an additive system. In Greek the symbol for one hundred was the letter H, and that for one thousand was the letter X, again repeated the number of times required (although the Greeks had symbols for five hundred and five thousand). The error of mistaking one hundred for one thousand in a translation or transcription from Egyptian into Greek would therefore have been one of mistaking one symbol for another, an error of translation, not an error of arithmetic. Plato states specifically that Solon examined the Egyptian records and translated them into Greek.

The result of applying this hypothesis to the story is to place the description of Atlantis and its fate not nine thousand, but nine hundred, years before Solon's visit to Egypt, or about 1450 b.c., which is in the middle of the Bronze Age date-bracket. How and why Galanopoulos came to have this idea and make this hypothesis must be reserved for a later section of this chapter. Here, however, attention may be paid to the application of the same hypothesis to another aspect of Plato's account. The great plain was described as 3,000 stadia in length and 2,000 stadia in width. These dimensions are equivalent to a length of 345 miles and a width of 230 miles, or nearly 80,000 square miles. The Greeks, whether Solon or Plato, must have realized that in the world as known to them, there could have been no room inside the Mediterranean for a land containing a plain of this size, and this must have been the reason why Solon or Plato placed Atlantis outside the Mediterranean, in the Atlantic Ocean, opposite the Pillars of Hercules or Strait of Gibraltar. But now, if the figures given by Plato for the linear dimensions of the great plain should have been ten times smaller, and expressed in hundreds instead of thousands, its length would become 34½ miles and its width 23 miles. Its area would become one hundred times smaller, or about 800 square miles. For a land of this order of size, there is room inside the Mediterranean.

For an objective appreciation of the story of Atlantis, it must be realized that it is an Egyptian account, as seen from the extreme eastern corner of the Mediterranean. For the early Egyptians, the Four

Pillars of the World were the boundaries, and originally these were mountains on the borders of Egypt itself. But when the Phoenicians opened up the western Mediterranean, and in 1100 b.c. founded Gades, now Cadiz, just outside the Strait of Gibraltar, an altar in the temple there became known as the Pillars of Hercules which, as Roger Dion has shown, played an important part not only in mythology, but in the psychological and theological warfare which the Greeks waged against their Phoenician rivals and enemies. At the same time, the Egyptian boundaries became idealized and enlarged, and pushed farther away to the west. This tendency seems to have underlain much of the Egyptian concept of Atlantis. Some reflection of this attitude must underlie the statement that after the disaster to Atlantis, and its disappearance beneath the waters of the sea, mud flats were left which impeded shipping on its way to the ocean. If Atlantis had gone down in the Atlantic Ocean, there would have been no mud flats left on the spot at the surface to impede any shipping. There would not have been any shipping there, in any case. But on the way from Egypt to the Strait of Gibraltar, which was the gate to the only ocean known to the ancients, there are quicksands in the bays of Syrtis Major and Syrtis Minor, off the northern shores of Tripolitania, which must have caused great inconvenience to ships that hugged the coast, as it is known that Egyptian seamen preferred to do. This is an indirect indication, based on geography and geology, that there must have been some notion of a location inside the Mediterranean for Atlantis.

Another geological argument follows from the statement that the cataclysm which engulfed Atlantis was also responsible for swallowing up an "Athenian" army under the earth. That Solon and Plato should have called this army "Athenian" at so remote a period was natural, much as King Arthur's army is now called "British" as if it had worn red coats. The essential point is that the army referred to by Plato was from mainland Greece, no doubt Mycenean, and this is significant, because seismic phenomena such as earthquakes do not manifest themselves with violence on the surface at great distances. In effect, and this applies whether the "Athenian" army was in Greece or in Atlantis, it restricts the distance between Greece and Atlantis, and confines the latter to the Mediterranean, and even to the eastern Mediterranean.

A similar conclusion is inevitable from a consideration of the political and material conditions that prevailed in the Bronze Age. Greek warriors might sail across a land-locked sea to fight against Troy, 200 miles away, but to imagine the Greeks mounting an expedition beyond the Strait of Gibraltar, 2,000 miles away, is impossible. There is no need to underline the absurdity of imagining a Bronze Age Greek army operating in or against Heligoland or Nigeria. Atlantis can have been only in the eastern Mediterranean.

The State of Atlantis Was the Minoan Empire

It was not before the beginning of the present century that Sir Arthur Evans started to excavate archaeological sites in Crete, and revealed a civilization and culture that were as unknown to modern scholarship as they had been to the classical Greeks. For Homer, Crete was typically Achaean Greek. Probably the first to draw attention to the close parallel between Plato's description of the institutions of his State of Atlantis and the newly revealed Minoan empire of Crete was K. T. Frost, who published an unsigned article in *The Times* which appeared on 19 February 1909. Four years later he amplified his account in the *Journal of Hellenic Studies* (vol. 33, 1913, p. 189).

The excavations in Crete revealed the enormous riches of the Minoan empire, accumulated through unrivalled sea power which gave the Minoans a prestige and a hegemony over the islands near Crete, southern Greece (i.e., part of Europe), and Libya (i.e., part of Africa). There is evidence from Herodotus that the Minoans undertook an expedition against Sicily, and it is known that they imported liparite from the Lipari Islands as a substitute for the obsidian glass from Melos. Their might must have been felt in the heel and toe of Italy, which later became the site of Greek colonies forming Magna Graecia, and so it might be said that their sway held up to the lands that later became subject to the Etruscans, which included the Campagnia behind Naples. In Plato's time the Etruscans' land was Tuscany.

The legendary tribute of boys and girls from Athens to Crete is a reflection of the Minoan supremacy over Greece. The commercial relations between Crete and Egypt were close enough for the Egyptians to take an interest in the Minoan empire which, centred on Crete, was in the far west so far as the Egyptians were concerned. The Egyptian name for Minoan Cretans, the Keftiu, shown in Egyptian tomb paintings, meant "men from the back of beyond."

These features of the Minoan empire may be compared with Plato's

State of Atlantis in some detail. In both there is great wealth produced by sea power, and redoubtable solidity and strength; products imported from abroad including "tribute" by sea in their ships to their harbours; well-equipped dockyards; a large fleet which made it unnecessary for them to fortify their ordinary towns; a high standard of living with baths and stadia; political domination over the islands of the Cyclades, parts of southern Greece and southern Italy and Sicily and over Libya. Plato's description of Atlantis as the way to other islands, from which it was possible to pass to the opposite continents, fits Crete perfectly.

There is a further feature in Plato's description of Atlantis which is really conclusive. The ceremony of the sacrifice of bulls by the princes of Atlantis, hunted with staves and nooses or nets but without the use of metallic weapons, accords exactly with what is known of Minoan practice, as illustrated in the finds at Knossos and depicted on the Vapheio gold cups. The sacrifices were made to Poseidon the Earthshaker who, as Homer said, "delights in bulls"; but he was also the titular deity of Atlantis, Plato says. Nowhere but in Minoan Crete could this have been found; and as all records of this civilization had been destroyed by the Myceneans and the Dorians, obliterated and forgotten, even by the time of Homer in whose eyes Cretans were mainly Achaean Greeks, Plato could not have invented these details. On the other hand, it would have been natural for the Egyptian records to have preserved them.

The great plain of Atlantis, described by Plato, next comes up for consideration. On Galanopoulos's hypothesis its dimensions were 34.5 miles in length and 23 miles in width. These are about the dimensions of the plain of Messara in Crete, open towards the sea on the south but surrounded on other sides by mountains. The existence of the plain of Messara in Crete is, of course, no evidence that it was the plain described by Plato in his story of Atlantis, just as the fact that an elephant can be led across a mountain pass does not make it Hannibal's; but if the Messara did not exist it would be necessary to construct additional hypotheses if it were desired to pursue the identity of the State of Atlantis with the Minoan empire.

The mineral resources of Crete include gold, silver, copper, and tin, which were the metals used in Atlantis. The plants and animals of Atlantis are appropriate for Crete, including the elephants, which may surprise the reader but which raises a knotty problem. Fossil remains of elephants were found in Crete in a cave near Retymno between Khama and Candia by Simonelli in 1893, and in 1904 Dorothea Bate found other remains in a cave near Cape Maleka, which shows that elephants lived on the island until recent geological times. These elephants have the additional interest that they were pygmies. It is one of the general consequences of the conditions of life on small islands, where the habitat of the descendants is reduced as compared with that of their ancestors, that the pressure exerted by natural selection is changed, and variation leads some animals, because of the absence of enemies, to become giants such as the tortoises on Galapagos or the Seychelles and the flightless birds of Madagascar and New Zealand, or very small as in the case of Shetland ponies or elephants in the Mediterranean islands—Sicily, Malta, Crete, Cyprus. The fact that these elephants are so small is in itself of interest, because it shows that they continued to live on their islands for a long enough time for this evolution to have taken place. It is believed that the area of the Aegean Sea was submerged, and Crete separated from Asia Minor, in Pleistocene times; but it is not known, and is even unlikely, that the elephants survived in Crete until the time when it was inhabited by man. If this was so, and if Atlantis was Crete, how did the Egyptians come to think that elephants had lived on the island?

That the elephant was well known to the Greeks is shown by the works of Aristotle. There is one further reason why the elephant is of interest in the history and mythology of the Greeks. An elephant skull has in the middle of its forehead a large circular and deep depression looking like an eye-socket, which is in fact the opening through which the cavity of the nose and trunk communicates with the cavity of the mouth. It is probable that the sight of such a skull was the origin of the Greek legend of the Cyclops. For this to have happened, it is not necessary that the elephants in the Mediterranean islands should have been contemporary there with man; trade between Greece and North Africa was sufficiently well developed for ivory, and therefore elephant skulls, to have become known to the Greeks, because elephants lived until comparatively recently in northern parts of Africa: in the West in Tunisia and Mauretania, in the East in Eritrea. They were the small forest variety of the African elephant which was used for military purposes in the armies of the Carthaginians and of the

Pharaohs. That the elephant was known in Egypt long before that time is shown by the Neolithic scratched representation of this animal at Salayah in the Libyan Desert, attributed to 4000 B.C. There is a picture of an elephant in a hieroglyphic reference to Elephantine City, and Amenemheb, who was in Syria with Thothmes III in 1470 B.C., recorded that he had been chased by an elephant. The elephant was therefore well known in Egypt from early times, but none of this can be taken as evidence that the Egyptians knew that there had been elephants in Crete; so these elephants cannot be used in support of the argument that the State of Atlantis included Crete.

There remain two historical aspects of Plato's story that need explanation if Atlantis is to be equated with the Minoan empire. One of these is the attempt by the State of Atlantis to attack Egypt by force of arms. There is no evidence of this having been attempted by the Minoans, but here it is necessary to suppose that with the passage of time after events that had taken place many centuries before, the mighty power of Minoan Crete had become confused with the attack on Egypt by the "Peoples of the Sea" in the thirteenth century B.C., when the invaders, who included post-Minoan Cretans, were defeated by Ramses II, as described in the inscriptions at Medinet Habu.

Finally, there is the ascription to the Athenians of a decisive victory over the State of Atlantis which saved the ancient world from domination by that State. This is where the legend of Theseus acquires its historical significance. The story goes that Theseus sailed from Athens to Crete, killed the Minotaur (who is easily recognized as the head of the Minoan empire), and broke the Minoan power, in virtue of which tribute in the form of boys and girls had been exacted from Athens. This event, which must have been based on a successful "Athenian," or at least Mycenaean, military expedition, is supposed to have taken place in the fourteenth century B.C.

Frost's conclusion, that "the long-lost Atlantis is neither more nor less than Minoan Crete," must therefore be regarded as a serious contribution to the solution of the problem. It was quickly supported by James Baikie, whose *Sea-Kings of Crete* was published in 1910, by D. A. Mackenzie (*Myths of Crete and Prehistoric Europe*) in 1917, and by J. D. S. Pendlebury (*The Archaeology of Crete*) in 1939. Charles Seltman (*History Today*, vol. 2, 1952, p. 332) is also favourable to this view. And yet there was still something missing from the interpretation of the story. If Crete, which still exists, formed part of the State of Atlantis, what was destroyed in the great and terrible cataclysm?

Frost skirts round this difficulty by assuming that what was suddenly destroyed was the Minoan empire rather than the island itself. As will be seen, there was without doubt a connexion between the destruction of the empire and a catastrophe, but Frost's hypothesis neglects the fact that in Plato's descriptions the State of Atlantis consisted of more than one island. In popular imagination it is common for islands to be thought of in the singular even when there may be more than one: Malta and Gozo, Zanzibar and Pemba, Madeira and Porto Santo. In each case, the pairs are known by the name of the former. In the case of Atlantis it was the smallest island, but, as the seat of the holiest shrine, the most important island, which came tragically and devastatingly to grief, as will now be seen.

The Catastrophe of Atlantis Was the Eruption of Santorin

The next stage in the unravelling of the mystery was reached by Spyridon Marinatos in 1939, when (*Antiquity,* vol. 13, p. 425) he considered the causes that could have brought about the abrupt collapse of Minoan power in the fifteenth century B.C., at the end of the period archaeologically known as Late Minoan I, generally put at about 1450 B.C. From the fact that the Minoan palace at Knossos was unfortified, a reflection of the efficacy of Minoan sea power, Sir Arthur Evans had abandoned the explanation that the Minoan empire succumbed directly to armed invasion, and leant towards the view that the end was due to catastrophic seismic causes. Marinatos then considered the fact that simultaneous destruction had affected the palaces of Knossos, Phaistos, and Mallia, the mansions of Hagia Triada, Tylissos, Nirou Khani, Sklavokampos, Amnisos and Apodoulu, the towns of Gournia, Palaikastro, Pseira and Zacri, and the cave of Arhalokhri, and he came to the conclusion that not only must a natural calamity have been responsible, but also that an ordinary earthquake could not have caused all this destruction, and therefore that a mighty volcanic eruption must have been responsible. He identified the volcano as that of Santorin, sixty miles north of Crete, an island that had been called *Kallistē,* the fairest of the Cyclades. This is the island which Marinatos has identified with the metropolis of Atlantis. Further evidence in support of this view has been obtained quite recently as a result of excavations in neighbouring islands, "Minoan colonies." The town which J. L. Caskey has excavated on Kea at Aghia Irini was destroyed at the same time as the Cretan palaces. The same is true of another town on Kythera.

The site of Santorin is now occupied by the crescent-shaped islands of Thera and Therasia, forming roughly a broken circle about 10 miles in diameter, enclosing a circular basin about 4 miles in diameter which represents the caldera of the old volcano, bordered by almost vertical precipitous sides 1,000 feet high. Marinatos was led to his conclusion that a volcano was responsible for the destruction because his excavations of Amnisos, the harbour town of Knossos, showed that it had been buried under pumice of volcanic origin.

O. G. S. Crawford, editor of *Antiquity,* salved his conscience after publishing Marinatos's article by inserting a note to the effect that "the main thesis of this article requires additional support." It was not long in coming. In 1956 an earthquake on Thera uncovered prehistoric walls and other objects near the town of Fira. Angelos Galanopoulos immediately visited the site and found, under layers of ashes 100 feet deep resting on the original surface soil, ruined walls 6 feet high, human bones and teeth, pottery, and charred pieces of the bark of trees. These remains were buried at the very start of a volcanic eruption, and carbon-14 estimations of their age, carried out at Columbia University, gave the figure of 3,370 years, plus or minus 100 years. Reckoning from 1957 when the work was done, this works out at about 1413 B.C. In order to avoid pretence at unattainable accuracy, a date of 1450 B.C. may be accepted as that of the start of the eruption, when pumice and ash first poured out of the volcano and must have taken the inhabitants by surprise because human beings were buried under them. The explosion of the volcano must have occurred a few years later.

It was the date of about 1450 B.C. for the eruption which suggested to Galanopoulos that as the catastrophe which put an end to the Minoan empire was about 900 years, not 9,000 years, before Solon's visit to Sais, an error of a factor of 10 had crept into the translation of the Egyptian records into the Greek texts. It may be seen from H. R. Hall's *Aegean Archaeology,* published in 1915, how much precision has been injected into the problem by an objective dating of 1450 B.C. for the eruption of Santorin, because fifty years ago a date of 2000 B.C. was generally adopted for that event.

Some idea of the effects of the explosion of a volcano that has left a caldera of the size of that of Santorin can be obtained from detailed descriptions of the eruption of Krakatau, a volcano on a small island in the Strait of Sunda, between Sumatra and Java, in 1883. On May 20 showers of fine ash began to fall, and on August 26 the explosion began. The quantity of volcanic ash blown into the air was so great that a large area was plunged into darkness in broad daylight at distances of 300 miles. Ash fell as far away as Australia, 1,500 miles away. The noise of the explosion was so loud that it was heard 3,000 miles away, in Indochina, Australia, the Philippines, and Japan. The explosion caused a displacement of water that gave rise to a tidal wave so high and powerful that it reached a height of 120 feet on the coasts of Java and Sumatra, and waves 50 feet high reached a mile inland. The disaster destroyed 295 towns and killed 36,000 people. Shipping was annihilated, and some ships, including a Dutch warship, were carried half a mile bodily inland. Where the volcano had previously existed was a chasm 150 metres deep beneath sea level. Five cubic miles of material had been blown out, and all that was left of Krakatau above the sea was three crescent-shaped islands, Verlaten, Lang, and Rakata, exactly like Thera and Therasia, the remnants of Santorin.

Terrible as was the destructive effect of the explosion of Krakatau, it has been calculated that as its caldera occupied an area of 23 square kilometres, whereas that of Santorin occupied 83 square kilometres and left a chasm 300 metres deep, the Santorin eruption must have been more than four times as destructive as that of Krakatau. This gives precision to the view to which Sir Arthur Evans came, that the Minoan empire came to an end as a result of a natural catastrophe, which can now be seen to have involved earthquakes, volcanic eruption and burial beneath ash and pumice, and tidal waves. In the palace of Minos at Knossos which Evans excavated, "The house of the fallen blocks" and "The house of the sacrificed oxen" were destroyed by blocks hurled southwards, which show that the shocks came from the north, the direction of Santorin. The tidal waves must have drowned all the inhabitants of the coast towns and harbours, and this gives point to the remark made by the priest of Sais to Solon, that only mountain-dwellers were left alive after the calamities that had occurred in Greek history. The Minoan fleets must have been destroyed and the political power of the Minoan State, which was based on command of the sea, shattered.

The fall of ash and pumice, the darkness, and the noise must have covered the whole of the eastern Mediterranean, including Lower Egypt and the delta of the Nile, where Sais was. As Galanopoulos has said, "The fantastic destruction caused by the Santorin eruption would have given the Egyptian scholars the impression that a whole continent had been destroyed." On the top of this must have come intelligence that the political situation had changed. Herodotus (VII, 171) remarks on Crete's having been devoid of inhabitants at one time.

Two points remain to be considered. One of these concerns the statement in Plato's account that an "Athenian" army was engulfed in the earth in the same cataclysm. There is no evidence to show where this army was, whether it was in Crete or in Greece. But the possibility of such a calamity in Greece itself is proved by the fate of the town of Helike, on the southern shore of the Gulf of Corinth, in 373 B.C., as described in detail by Pausanias (VII, xxiv, 6). The town was completely destroyed in one night by an earthquake and a tidal wave in such a way that everything—houses, people, ships in the harbour— was covered up by earth and mud, as it remains to this day. Rescue squads sent out by neighbouring states on the day following the disaster found nothing left at all. This is why such high hopes are entertained of what Spyridon Marinatos will find of a completely preserved city which was destroyed during the lifetimes of Plato, Aristotle, Epaminondas, and Praxiteles.

Before the original island of Santorin can be accepted as part of the State of Atlantis, if the latter is to be equated with the Minoan empire, it is necessary that Santorin, or its successors Thera and Therasia, should show evidence of Minoan culture and civilization. This evidence is forthcoming. An eruption on Thera in 1866 revealed the existence of Bronze Age remains, buried beneath 100 feet of ashes, and other finds show that pottery on Santorin was Minoan, but about fifty years older than that discovered in the ruined sites in Crete. This may mean that there was more than one eruption of Santorin, or, as M. S. F. Hood has expressed it, that the islands around Crete showed a "provincial" and retarded form of Minoan civilization. In any case,

Santorin clearly belonged to the same political unit as Crete until the catastrophe.

Even more significant are the results of excavations still in progress on Thera, conducted by James Mavor and Emily Vermuele. Near the village of Akrotiri, they have found buried under 30 to 50 feet of ashes the remains of a complete city, estimated to have contained 30,000 people. Some of the buildings, two and three storeys high, are intact. The settlement was Minoan.

Finally, one small point. Plato's description of the metropolis of Atlantis showed that there was a hot spring there. Hot springs are evidence of volcanic activity.

It is hoped that this short analysis of the story of Atlantis, which is to form the subject of a forthcoming work by Angelos Galanopoulos who has done so much to unravel its mystery, will have sufficed to show that it can no longer be dismissed as a fairy tale, and that there is sufficient internal evidence in Plato's account, and circumstantial evidence from other sources, to allow the conclusion to be drawn that the story of Atlantis was historically based on the Minoan empire of Crete and the neighbouring islands, and that the violent end of one of these islands, and of the political Minoan state, is attributable to a natural catastrophe that took place in the fifteenth century B.C.

Atlantis and Submarine Archaeology

In addition to the disappearance beneath the waters of what was probably the metropolis of Atlantis, there is another reason why it is particularly appropriate to associate the subject with submarine archaeology. This is because its chief character, Solon, was involved in what was probably the earliest recorded case of submarine archaeology. Plutarch has related how the fishermen of Cos had sold their catch in advance to some business speculators of Miletus, before they hauled up a golden tripod from the sea in their nets. Nobody familiar with Homer can fail to appreciate the enormous importance of such a find, even if the explanation be discounted that this particular tripod had been thrown overboard by Helen on her return journey from Troy to Greece. The disposal of the tripod in the fishermen's nets led to a dispute, over which the Coans and the Miletans went to war. The Pythian priestess of Apollo intervened and proclaimed that the tripod must be presented to the wisest of men. Solon himself was one of the seven sages, all of whom, in turn, were wise enough to refuse to accept it.

If the explanation of the story of Atlantis be as outlined above, it is, however, not clear how much of the history of Atlantis remains beneath the sea, because so much of Santorin must have been blown into thin air. In 1962 Professor Otschakovsky, in the Soviet research ship *Academician Vavilov,* dredged samples of rock from the sea-bed near Thera for physical and chemical tests, the results of which are awaited. What seems to be required in this case is something more than dredging or exploration of the sea bottom. If the layer of ashes is 100 feet thick, as it is on Thera, submarine excavation will be required to uncover the walls surrounding the palace and temple of the metropolis of Atlantis, if they are still extant, sunk beneath the sea. If, however, as recent excavations show, the ashes of Thera and Therasia cover such ancient buildings, the work will not be so difficult, and further results will be awaited with eager expectation.

CHAPTER

12

Vinland:
Norsemen Land in America

Yale University Press has recently published a beautiful reproduction and analysis of a map drawn in the middle of the fifteenth century, showing to the west of Greenland a large area of land labelled Vinland. The palaeographic evidence, as shown by Thomas E. Marston of Yale after a meticulous investigation, is that the handwriting on the map and the accompanying manuscript, the paper of the manuscript, and the binding are clearly datable to about A.D. 1440, around fifty years before Columbus's voyage to America. The cartographic evidence, as was shown by R. A. Skelton of the British Museum after an analysis no less searching, confirms this and makes it possible to go farther and to say that if this map had been drawn after Columbus's voyages at the end of the fifteenth century, it would inevitably have shown far more than it does show, which can only represent traditionally preserved reports of landfalls and desultory exploration in North America, such as those which the Norsemen are well known to have made in the tenth and eleventh centuries, five hundred years before Columbus.

The publication of the Vinland map has had three curious results. One has been an outburst of indignation on the part of some of Columbus's countrymen, about which the least said the better. The second has been a negative reaction on the part of a few experts who, however, fail to agree among themselves. While some claim that the map is genuine, but post-Columbian, others deny that it is anything other than a modern forgery. There are pitfalls here into which those who are neither professional palaeographers nor cartographers should avoid falling. But it is pertinent to ask, and reasonable to hope, that the discussion will take place in the light of the evidence presented by examination of the map itself, and not of reproductions of it. An example of the dangers attending neglect of this precaution is provided by the argument that has been advanced on the strength of what in a newspaper reproduction appeared to be a small island just south of Greenland, an island which in fact, in the map itself, is only a worm-hole. It seems that there always are, and always will be, nonconformists on even the most clear-cut issues; there have been opponents to Michael Ventris's decipherment of the Linear Minoan B script, and some are still incapable of appreciating the evidence that evolution is a fact. Perhaps there may be people who believe that the earth is flat, and that the sun moves round it.

The third result of the publication has been to show how widespread is the ignorance that prevails generally on the evidence for the discovery of North America by Norsemen in the tenth and eleventh centuries, five hundred years before Columbus. This evidence stands irrefutable, whether the Vinland map is genuine or not. It is documentary and chiefly contained in three mediaeval manuscripts preserved in the Royal Library of Copenhagen, which describe the colonization of Iceland and of Greenland. One of these manuscripts, known as *Hauk's Book*, was written partly in his own hand, and as he died in 1334 it can be dated to the early fourteenth century. There is a manuscript copy of it in an early fifteenth-century hand. The second manuscript is the *Saga of Eric the Red*, which was written later than *Hauk's Book* but the text of which is based on an earlier version; both are Icelandic.

The third manuscript is the *Flatey Book*, compiled for John Haakonson, who was born in 1350; it is datable between 1370 and 1387. This version, which differs in some respects from the other two, was probably Greenlandic, and the differences must have resulted from the fact that contact between Iceland and Greenland was lost at the end of the thirteenth century when trade with Iceland was made a Norwegian crown monopoly. All these texts have been translated and commented on by G. M. Gathorne-Hardy in a book, *The Norse Discoverers of America*, published nearly fifty years ago.

The texts describe the settlement of Iceland and of Greenland, as well as voyages resulting in discovery of land to the west of Greenland, and as the good faith of the description of the settlement of Greenland has been substantiated by archaeology as well as by history, there is no reason to disparage the objective nature of the descriptions of the voyages. Before dealing with these, however, it must be pointed out that the climatic conditions that prevailed in Iceland and Greenland at the time of the settlement a thousand years ago were not the same as those of today. This is known from a number of lines of scientific research, among the most demonstrative of which were those carried out by J. D. H. Wiseman and C. D. Ovey in the British Museum (Natural History) on chemical and biological analysis of cylindrical cores, obtained from the bottom of the middle of the Atlantic Ocean, near the equator, at a depth of over 2,000 fathoms, by B. Kullenberg and Hans Pettersson of the Swedish Deep-Sea Expedition.

The chemical analysis is based on the fact that the productivity of small marine organisms with calcareous shells such as foraminifera is dependent on temperature, and as these shells are constantly falling to the bottom of the ocean as the organisms die, the relative concentrations of carbonate at different levels of the core indicate changes of temperature in surface waters where the organisms lived. The biological analysis takes account of the fact that different species of foraminifera are adapted to live within narrow temperature-brackets; some of them are tropical, others arctic, species, and as they can be recognized in the cores, they also provide indications of the temperature at the surface at the time of deposition.

To these methods may be added a third, credited to H. C. Urey of the University of California, who showed that the abundance of the isotope oxygen-18 in calcium carbonate depends on the temperature at which it is deposited, and so the ratio between oxygen-18 and the normal oxygen-16 can be used as a sort of geological thermometer. Results obtained by all these methods show that there was a climatic optimum beginning about A.D. 950 and ending about A.D. 1250, the dates being obtained by calculating the rate of deposition at the bottom of the ocean and translating this into different levels in the core. This time-bracket of higher temperature is precisely that during which the Norsemen started their settlement in Greenland, and their abandonment of some of their settlements coincided with the fall in temperature in the fourteenth century. Evidence that the soil was not frozen, at least during the summer months, is provided by botany, for coffins in cemeteries have been found to have been penetrated by roots of plants. Even so, Greenland still had icy mountains and glaciers during the climatic optimum, and the point is important because they enabled the Norsemen to recognize it when they had got home to Greenland.

Iceland was settled about A.D. 870 when Ingolf came there from Norway, although Irish monks had already been there for 100 years. Thenceforth, Iceland became the advanced base from which Norsemen set out on exploring expeditions, and in 982 Eric the Red discovered Greenland. Four years later he returned thither, with women, horses, cattle and all, to found a permanent colony, with an eastern settlement near Julianehaab, not far from Cape Farewell, and, soon afterwards, a western settlement near Godthaab, further north.

In the same year, 986, Bjarni Herjulfsson sailed from Iceland intending to reach Greenland, where his father Herjulf had settled at Herjulfness; but he was blown off his course by northerly gales into an area of fog and was completely lost for many days, drifting. Eventually he made a landfall, but the land (Bjarni's "First Land") could not have been the Greenland for which he was hoping because it was covered with woods and small knolls. Leaving this land on his port side, he sailed for two days and came to a Second Land, but this was flat and wooded and lacked the glaciers that he knew were to be seen in Greenland. He sailed away again with a south-west wind and came to a Third Land, high, mountainous, icy and barren, but Bjarni did not believe that it was Greenland. With the same south-west wind he set out to sea again and sailed for four more days, after which he arrived at Herjulfness where his father was.

Bjarni's voyage when blown off his course was therefore quite accidental, but he had sighted three lands south-west of Greenland, and the prospects of further exploration excited his countrymen in Greenland, particularly Leif Ericson, son of Eric the Red. Leif sailed about the year 1002 with a crew including a German called Tyrker who played a significant part in the voyage. They first came to what they took to be Bjarni's Third Land, high, with a background of ice between which and the sea there was nothing but flat bare rock, and they called it Helluland, the Land of Flat Stone. Next they came to what they took to be Bjarni's Second Land, low-lying with stretches of white sand and wooded, for which reason they called it Markland (Woodland). Sailing away again with a north-east wind for two days, they came to, and landed on, an island near the mainland and then sailed into the sound between the island and the mainland. The water was so shallow that the ship ran aground, but they managed to get it off and sailed up the mouth of a river, where they landed and built houses in which to pass the winter. There was grass with dew, the grass did not wither, there was no frost, large quantities of salmon abounded, the lengths of day and night were more evenly divided than in Greenland or even Iceland, and on the shortest day the sun was higher in the sky at breakfast time and at nones than in Iceland. Leif and his men explored the country, and the German Tyrker came back laden with vines and grapes. When asked how he knew what these were, Tyrker replied that where he was brought up in his youth, in Germany, there was no lack of vines and grapes. Leif therefore called this land Vinland. There were also "mösur" trees so big that they could be used for house-building. After filling his ship with vines and grapes, he sailed back to Greenland.

The story then turns to the exploits of Leif's brother, Thorvald Ericson, who sailed about the year 1004 and came to Vinland and wintered there. In the spring he sailed into the mouth of a river to a wooded headland where he landed and saw three canoes upside down with three savages, "skraelings," under each of them. The Norsemen killed eight, and one escaped with a canoe. Soon afterwards a large number of canoes appeared and a battle took place. The skraelings rained arrows on the Norsemen and mortally wounded Thorvald, who was buried on the headland. The survivors then returned to Vinland where they wintered before returning to Greenland with their ship full of grapes and vines.

The most important expedition of all was led about 1019 by Thorfinn Karlsefni, who sailed from Iceland to Greenland. In the following year Karlsefni sailed first to the Western Settlement, and then for two days with a north wind to a land with large stones and many arctic foxes. This he identified with Helluland. Sailing two days more with a north wind, he and his crew reached a land with many woods and many beasts, where, on an island, they killed a bear. This land they identified with Markland. Continuing to sail for two days, leaving the coast on their starboard side, they came to a shore with a very long beach. Karlsefni's crew included two Scots, Hake and Hekja, who were reputed fast runners. They were put ashore with instructions to explore southwards for three days, after which time they returned, one carrying grapes and the other ears of wild corn. This was Vinland. They then sailed into a sound and wintered there.

They explored the neighbourhood, found grasslands and mountains, and a whale of a kind unknown to them which was stranded. Karlsefni sailed southwards and came to a river mouth where there were fields of wild unsown corn on lower ground, vines on higher ground, and an abundance of fish and beasts. One day nine canoes hove in sight, manned by men who waved staves that made a noise like threshing. The skraelings came ashore, swarthy, ugly, unkempt, with large eyes and broad cheeks, and then went away. No snow fell, and Karlsefni's cattle remained in the open, finding their own pasture. In the spring a fleet of canoes came from the south up the estuary, and the skraelings showed that they wanted to trade, offering skins and grey furs in exchange for which they wanted red cloth, which they bound round their heads. One of Karlsefni's bulls then started to bellow, and the terrified skraelings raced back to their canoes. Three weeks later an armada of skraeling canoes returned and there was a battle. The skraelings rained missiles including arrows and sling-stones, and they also used a curious weapon looking like a dark globe fixed to the end of a pole, which was brought crashing down with great noise. Eventually the savages withdrew, but Karlsefni and his men had had enough and decided to sail away. They coasted northwards and came across five savages wearing skins and carrying food-vessels containing bone-marrow mixed with blood, whom they killed.

Sailing with a south wind, they came to Markland, where they found five savages—one man, two women, and two boys—whom they captured, after which they returned to Greenland.

In the last of these expeditions, led by Eric's daughter Freydis in 1024, she persuaded two men, Helgi and Finnbogi, to accompany her in their ship while she sailed in hers. The bait was the profit that they expected to make out of what they brought back from Vinland, which was to be shared. The expedition was ill-fated, for after wintering, Freydis murdered Helgi and Finnbogi and returned to Greenland.

This exhausts the accounts of the chief voyages described in the manuscripts mentioned, but other manuscripts provide further information about the lands found south-west of Greenland. Quoting what had been told him by King Sweyn Estrithson of Denmark, who died in 1075, Adam of Bremen, in his *Description* of the islands or countries of the north, said that there was an island called Vinland because vines grew there naturally and also corn without having been sown. The *Icelandic Annals* for the year 1121 stated that Eric Gnupsson, Bishop of Greenland, set out for Vinland. Writing was introduced into Iceland by Ari the Learned, who was born in 1067 and died in 1148. His grandfather was a cousin of Karlsefni's, and his uncle informed him about Eric. In his *Islendlingabok*, Ari mentioned the Skraelings who lived in Vinland, and he was also partly responsible for the *Landnamabok*, which mentioned Karlsefni, who was described as the discoverer of Vinland the Good. The *Icelandic Annals* for the year 1347 stated that a ship arrived from Greenland with a crew who had been to Markland.

On the basis of all these accounts, attempts have been made to identify the actual landfalls of the Norse voyagers. The speed at which they sailed, and the distance covered in what was described as a day's sailing, have been estimated from fifteenth-century manuscripts describing voyages from Norway to Iceland and from Iceland to Greenland, and worked out at about 150 nautical miles a day. Taking account of this, the directions of the winds indicated, local currents, and the prevalence of fog off the Newfoundland Banks, Gathorne-Hardy identified Bjarni Herjulfsson's First Land as the Barnstable Peninsula in Massachusetts, his Second Land as Nova Scotia, and his Third Land as Newfoundland. These are then equated with Leif Ericson's Vinland, Markland, and Helluland, respectively. Attempts have been made at identification in greater detail of places mentioned in the manuscripts, but they can only be conjectural and need not be considered here. Nor is it necessary to believe that the lands called Helluland, Markland, and Vinland by the different voyagers meant identically the same locality in each case. The inescapable conclusions are:

First, there was land, found to the south and south-west of Greenland. Next, some of the landfalls, Markland and Vinland, were timber-rich countries which Greenland was not. Vinland contained vines and wild corn, and here the reports of later voyagers can be consulted with profit. Jacques Cartier, Samuel de Champlain, Charles Leigh, and Henry Hudson found wild corn or vines in the lands visited by them. With regard to skraelings or Red Indians, Jacques Cartier reported that they were in the habit of turning canoes upside down and sleeping under them; Nicolas Denys found that the Indians in Nova Scotia ate grease extracted from moose bones, a form of pemmican, which agrees with the described contents of the food-vessels found with the skraelings by Karlsefni; and Henry Hudson reported that the Indians of Cape Cod brought beaver skins and fine furs for which they wanted red gowns in exchange. The waving staves that made a noise like threshing can be equated with the rattle-sticks which the Indians used; the curious weapon on a pole appears to tally with an implement used by the Algonquins, who sewed boulders into skins and attached them to poles; and as for the stranded whale of a species unknown to Karlsefni, whales play a prominent part in the legends of the Indians of New England. That the lands in question, wherever they were, lay to the south of Greenland is indisputable from the distribution of vines, a species of *Vitis,* the wild corn to which, on the data, it is impossible to ascribe a species, the greater equivalence of the lengths of days and nights, and the greater height of the sun on the shortest day, which must place Leif Ericson's Vinland south of the Saint Lawrence River. On all these counts the Norsemen certainly discovered land, and that land can only have been North America.

With the deterioration of climate in the fourteenth century the deeds of the Greenland Norsemen faded into obscurity and oblivion, and with the abandonment of many of their settlements and the climate-enforced interruption of traffic between Greenland and Norway in the opening years of the fifteenth century, the Norsemen's knowledge of lands in the west was lost to European map-makers. It is curious that they did not share it earlier, for after the conversion of Icelanders and Greenlanders to Christianity in the eleventh century, and therefore after the discovery of American lands, Norse pilgrims and scholars on their way to Rome were numerous. In 1151 Nicolaus Seemundarsson, Abbot of Thingeyrar, author of the *Icelandic Itinerary,* passed through Basel, and that was precisely the place to which all the evidence points for the production of the Vinland Map of about 1440, when the Council of Basel was in session.

As writing did not make its appearance in Iceland until one hundred years after the Norsemen's voyages, the tradition was solely oral in its transmission for many generations, and no geographical precision is to be expected from the Vinland Map, or from its Norse precursor from which it must have been copied. The legends written on it, however, make welcome reading: *Vinlanda Insula a Byarno reperta et leipho socijs, Bjarni Herjulfsson and Leif Ericsson.* This is followed by a longer legend to the effect that Bjarni and Leif, sailing southwards from Greenland, discovered an unknown land, rich and fertile even to the point of having vines, which they called Vinland. It goes on to refer to the visit made in the last year of Pope Paschal II, therefore in 1118, by Eric Gnupsson, Papal Legate and Bishop of Greenland and Distant Regions, to Vinland, where he stayed for a year before returning north-eastwards to Greenland. This circumstantial information may imply that there was a colony of Norsemen living in Vinland to whom the bishop had pastoral duties.

Botany adds one more little piece of evidence in support of the documents, for Nicholas Polunin has pointed out that some plants that persist in Greenland can only have been originally brought there from America. Bogus archaeology, on the other hand, has only provided a number of false clues, among which may be mentioned the turkeys depicted in an allegedly thirteenth-century frieze in Schleswig Cathedral, which is much more recent; a so-called Viking grave at Beardmore in Ontario, containing objects brought in recently; and a fourteenth-century date attributed to the Newport Tower in Rhode Island, which was built in Colonial times. On the other hand, a genuine mediaeval Scandinavian settlement has been found recently in Newfoundland, but the results are not yet published.

As in the case of other historical problems, that of the Norsemen's discovery and voyages to North America is accessible to the results of investigations in natural science, to which meteorology, astronomy, and botany have all contributed. The scientific proof of the existence of a climatic optimum beginning about A.D. 950 is important for three reasons. In the first place, it enabled Greenland to be settled. Second, the probability that the Arctic Ocean was then relatively free from polar ice (the descriptions of the Norsemen's voyages make no mention of ice as a hindrance to navigation) is relevant to the question whether they may not have sailed farther north than is imagined, a point which bears on the mapping of the northern shore of Greenland in the Vinland map. Finally, the fact that the climate and temperature have deteriorated since the thirteenth century will have to be taken into account in any attempt to repeat the voyages of the Norsemen at the present day; Eric the Red's route due west from Iceland to Greenland would be impracticable, and the prevalent winds and ocean currents may now be different from what they then were.

The documents, even without the Vinland Map, are sufficient to accord a true bill to the Norse discovery of America, but it is really an insult to the memory of Christopher Columbus to suppose that the Norsemen's deeds detract in the slightest degree from his achievement. Nationalistic searches for priority can have disconcerting results. Attempts have now been made to show that the Etruscans first sailed to America. As the Etruscans did not reach Italy from Asia Minor much before the tenth century B.C., and their sea power was utterly shattered by Hiero I of Syracuse in 474 B.C. at the battle off Cumae, their marine exploits were confined within the period when the Phoenicians held the Strait of Gibraltar against all comers. If priority is so important, it must be accorded to those offspring of the Mongol stock who crossed the Bering isthmus shortly after the end of the last Ice Age, about 35,000 years ago, and gave rise to the Eskimo and Amerindians. Carbon-14 estimations of charcoal from Amerindian hearths in Lewisville, Texas, give a date of 33,000 B.C. Nor does this detract from the prowesses of the Norsemen.

Postscript

It once fell to me to hand to Dr. Agnes Arber, a great botanist and a great lady, the Gold Medal of the Linnean Society of London. Among the few words which she spoke in acknowledgement and thanks, she told the story of an old family servant whom she was so fortunate as to have for running and looking after her home. Coming into her study and seeing her deeply engaged, as she had seen her day after day for years, the servant said disapprovingly to Dr. Arber, "You work and you work and you work, and when you have done it, what is it?" This is a question which I frequently ask myself, but I do not know the answer.

For one thing, I do not know why I work, as I have now done for nearly fifty years, except that I enjoy it. Some of the things that have given me the greatest pleasure are so trivial that they have little importance at all, as when I succeed in identifying some person who has been anonymous, either an author of a book, or the man who advised Jean Jacques Rousseau to leave Switzerland, or the American who came back there and had the rare distinction of having known both Voltaire and Madame de Staël personally.

Perhaps my enjoyment stems partly from the comfortable miserly feeling of avoiding waste, when anything that is learnt or discovered in one subject helps another. As I have tried to show in one of the chapters of this book, genetics is so closely connected with all the other sciences that advances in any of them help genetics. The study of problems concerning Voltaire helps to solve those of Rousseau and reciprocally; the same is true of Byron and Shelley. There is a curious satisfaction in running two or more subjects in parallel and finding that they connect. This is why it is so fascinating to read a book and at the same time follow the story on a map. I find the same pleasure in running Darwin, Mendel, and Fisher, and the principles for which they were responsible: evolution, natural selection, and genetics.

But the daisy-chain extends farther than that, for natural science can be used to study and solve problems outside science itself, such as those of the prehistory of Western Europe, the location of Atlantis, and the Norse discoverers of America. I have previously done the same thing for the puzzles of the origin of the Etruscans, the tin-trade of Cornwall, Hannibal's route across the Alps, and the sex-life of Edward Gibbon. I find myself looking at a vast horizon of questions on a front in which any advance may help other sectors.

I have avoided the situation which Darwin regretted so much when he said, "It is an accursed evil to a man to become so absorbed in any subject as I am in mine," meaning that he had only one. That is why he was so outstandingly successful in it. I am more selfish.

Notes

CHAPTER 1
pages 25–45

1. Letter from Isaac Newton to Robert Hooke, 5 February 1675/6, *The Correspondence of Isaac Newton,* ed. W. H. Turnbull, Cambridge, 1959, vol. 1, p. 416. I am indebted for this reference to Professor E. N. da C. Andrade. F.R.S. Newton did not originate this expression. A correspondence initiated by George Sarton in *Isis* (1935–36, **24,** 107) and answered by R. E. Ockenden (*ibid.,* 1936, **25,** 451) and R. Klibansky (*ibid.,* 1936–37, **26,** 147) reveals that it is traceable back to the twelfth century, and the idea to Bernard of Chartres and to Seneca. I am indebted to Dr. Angus Armitage for these references.

2. D. McKie and G. de Beer, "Newton's Apple," *Notes & Records of the Royal Society,* 1952, **9,** 46 and 333.

3. Gavin de Beer, *Science and the Humanities,* The Rickman Godlee Lecture, University College, London (H. K. Lewis), 1956.

4. D. McKie, "Wöhler's Synthesis of Urea and the Rejection of Vitalism: A Chemical Legend," *Nature,* 1944, **153,** 608.

5. W. S. MacLeay, *Horae Entomologicae,* London, 1819–21.

6. E. Newman, *Sphinx vespiformis: An Essay,* London, 1832, p. 15.

7. Gavin de Beer, "The Origins of Darwin's Ideas on Evolution and Natural Selection," *Proc. Roy. Soc. Lond.,* B., 1961, **155,** 321. See p. 46 *supra.*

8. "Darwin's Notebooks on Transmutation of Species," ed. Sir Gavin de Beer, III, *Bull. Brit. Mus. (Nat. Hist.),* Historical Series, 1960, **2,** 138.

9. Charles Darwin, *Autobiography,* ed. Nora Barlow, London, 1958, p. 118; "Darwin's Ornithological Notes," ed. Nora Barlow, *Bull. Brit. Mus. (Nat. Hist.),* Historical Series, 1963, **2,** 201.

10. Gavin de Beer, "Darwin's Notebooks on Transmutation of Species," I, *Bull. Brit. Mus. (Nat. Hist.),* Historical Series, 1960, **2,** 58, 60.

11. *Ibid.,* II, p. 114; III, p. 141.

12. Edward Blyth, "On Psychological Distinctions Between Man and Other Animals; and the Consequent Diversity of Human Influence over the Inferior Ranks of Creation, from any Mutual and Reciprocal Influence Exercised Among the Latter," *Mag. Nat. Hist.,* New Series, 1837, **1,** 135 (reprinted in *Proc. Amer. Phil. Soc.,* 1959, **103,** 147).

13. Montesquieu, *Œuvres Complètes,* éditions de la Pléiade, Paris, t.1, 1956, p. 1188.

14. Maupertuis, *Vénus Physique,* Paris, 1745; *Essai sur la formation des êtres organisés,* Paris, 1754 (*v.* Jean Rostand, *L'évolution des aspèces. Histoire des idées transformistes,* Paris, 1932, p. 26).

15. Denis Diderot, *De l'Interprétation de la nature,* Paris, 1753; *Œuvres philosophiques,* Paris (Garnier), 1961, p. 187.

16. "Baumann" [= Maupertuis], *Dissertatio inauguralis metaphysica de universali naturae systemate pro gradu doctoris habita,* Erlangen, 1751 (*v.* Rostand, *loc. cit.*).

17. Gavin de Beer, "Alexander Moritzi," *Ann. Sci.*, 1960 [1962], **16**, 25.

18. Letter from Charles Darwin to Baden Powell, "Some Unpublished Letters of Charles Darwin," ed. Sir Gavin de Beer, *Notes & Records of the Royal Society*, 1959, **14**, 52, 53.

19. Darwin's Notebooks, I, *loc. cit.*, p. 46.

20. *Ibid.*, p. 65.

21. Darwin's Notebooks II, *loc. cit.*, p. 99.

22. T. R. Malthus, *Essay on the Principle of Population*, London, 1826 (the 6th edition, which was in Darwin's possession; *v. Catalogue of the Library of Charles Darwin* . . . , compiled by H. W. Rutherford, Cambridge, 1908), vol. 1, p. 6.

23. The note is on pp. 134 and 135 which were excised by Darwin from his Notebook III; it was recognized among the papers of the late Bernard Darwin by Miss Maria Skramovsky of the British Museum (Natural History). The pages are so extensively interlined that the order of the sentences must to some extent be conjectural.

24. Charles Darwin, *Autobiography*, *op. cit.*, p. 120.

25. L. Z. Freedman and A. Roe, *Behavior and Evolution*, ed. Anne Roe and George Gaylord Simpson, New Haven (Yale), 1959, p. 473.

26. W. Hazlitt, *The Spirit of the Age*, London, 1825 (World's Classics, London, Grant Richards, 1904, p. 147). I am indebted for this reference to Mr. W. T. McLeod.

27. *King John*, III, 1, 273–277.

28. Conway Zirkle, "Natural Selection before the 'Origin of Species,'" *Proc. Amer. Phil. Soc.*, 1941, **84**, 71.

29. W. C. Wells, *Two Essays upon Double and Single Vision etc.*, London, 1818 (*v.* C. Zirkle, *loc. cit.*); C. A. Kofoid, "An American Pioneer in Science, Dr. William Charles Wells, 1758–1817," *Scientific Monthly*, 1943, **57**, 77; R. H. Shryock, "The Strange Case of Wells'

Theory of Natural Selection (1813): Some Comments on the Dissemination of Scientific Ideas," *Studies & Essays in the History of Science . . . in homage to George Sarton*, ed. M. F. Ashley Montagu, New York, 1944, p. 197.

30. Patrick Matthew, *Naval Timber and Arboriculture*, London, 1831 (*v.* C. Zirkle, *loc. cit.*).

31. Charles Lyell, *Principles of Geology*, London, 1832, vol. ii, p. 175.

32. Edward Blyth, *loc. cit.*, p. 79 (reprinted in *Proc. Amer. Phil. Soc.*, 1959, **103**, 142).

33. Loren C. Eiseley, "Charles Darwin, Edward Blyth, and the Theory of Natural Selection," *Proc. Amer. Phil. Soc.*, 1959, **103**, 94.

34. Charles Lyell, *op. cit.*, p. 131.

35. Theodosius Dobzhansky, "Blyth, Darwin, and Natural Selection," *American Naturalist*, 1959, **93**, 204.

36. Gavin de Beer, "Mendel, Darwin, and Fisher," *Notes & Records of the Royal Society*, 1964, **19**, 192.

37. Gregor Mendel, "Versuche über Pflanzen-Hybriden," *Verhandl. Naturforsch. Ges. Brünn*, 1865, **4**, Abhandlungen, 1886, p. 3.

38. R. A. Fisher, "Has Mendel's Work Been Rediscovered?" *Ann. Sci.*, 1936, **1**, 115.

39. *Hamlet*, II, 1, 63–66.

40. G. de Morsier et M. Cramer, "Jean-Antoine Colladon et la découverte de la loi de l'hybridation en 1821," *Gesnerus*, 1959, **16**, 113. Colladon's work was referred to by name by Prosper Lucas in *Traité de l'hérédité naturelle*, Paris and London, 1847, t.1, p. 212; also by William Frédéric Edwards in *Caractère physiologique des races humaines*, Paris, 1829, p. 26. I am indebted to Professor G. de Morsier for these references. Darwin referred to these publications in *Variations of Animals and Plants* . . . , 1st edition, London, 1868, vol. 2, pp. 92 and 87 respectively, under the names of their authors, and from Lucas he quoted Colladon's results

on mice but without mentioning Colladon's name. Mendel could therefore have known of Colladon's results in 1868 (three years after reading his paper) but would not have found his name there. In the 2nd edition (1875) of Darwin's *Variation*, the account of breeding experiments with mice is included (vol. ii, p. 70), but with a statement that in addition to grey and white mice, piebald mice were obtained. The origin of this insertion, which contradicts Colladon's results, has not been traced.

41. Augustin Sageret, "Considérations sur la production des hybrides . . . ," *Annales des sciences naturelles*, 1826, **8**, 294.

42. Charles Naudin, "Nouvelles recherches sur l'hybridité dans les végétaux," *Ann. Sci. nat. Bot.*, Paris, 1863, **19**, 180.

43. Jean Rostand, *L'atomisme en biologie*, Paris, 1956, p. 46.

44. E. B. Ford, "Genetic Research in the Lepidoptera," *Ann. Eugen.*, 1940, **10**, 227.

45. R. A. Fisher, "The Bearing of Genetics on Theories of Evolution," *Sci. Progress*, 1932, **27**, 2.

46. George G. Simpson, *The Major Features of Evolution*, New York, 1953.

47. Oxford at the Clarendon Press, 1930.

48. P. B. Medawar, "Imagination and Hypothesis," *Times Literary Supplement*, 25 October 1953, p. 849.

49. John Ruskin, *Ariadne Florentina*, in *Works*, London, 1906, vol. xxii, p. 396. I am indebted to Dr. Sydney Ross for this reference.

50. J. Bousquet, "Un statère d'or de Cyrène sur la Côte du Finistère," *Comptes Rendus de l'Académie des inscriptions et belles-lettres de l'année 1960*, 1961, p. 317.

51. D. King-Hele, *Erasmus Darwin*, London, 1963, p. 145.

52. Joseph Conrad, *Some Reminiscences*, London, 1912.

53. Claudine Chonez, *Giono par lui-même*, Paris (Editions du Seuil), 1959, p. 35.

54. S. T. Coleridge, *Anima Poetæ*, ed. E. H. Coleridge, London, Heineman, 1895, p. 244.

55. J. L. Lowes, *The Road to Xanadu*, London, Constable [1930], p. 12.

56. *Ibid.*, p. 63.

57. R. W. Emerson.

CHAPTER 2

pages 46–66

1. Ed. Nora Barlow, 1958.

2. *Nature, Lond.*, **184**, 1102, 1959.

3. *Autobiographies*, p. 270, 1897.

4. *Gibbon's Journey from Geneva to Rome*, 1961.

5. *Mélanges Gilliard*, p. 400, Lausanne, 1944.

6. 1934 (abbr. *Diary*).

7. *Charles Darwin and the Voyage of the Beagle*, 1945 (abbr. *Beagle*).

8. *Beagle*, p. 246.

9. 1839, repr. 1952 (abbr. *J. of R.*).

10. *Impulse*, Nov. 1959, p. 2; *Victorian Studies*, Bloomington, Ia., 3, 109, 1959.

11. *Bull. Brit. Mus. (Nat. Hist.)*, Historical Series, 1960, **2**, 23, 75, 119, 151, **3**, 129 (abbr. *Notebook*, followed by no. of Notebook in roman and reference to MS page of Notebook in arabic figures).

12. *Ibid.*, **2**, 1, 1959 (abbr. *Journ.*).

13. *Evolution by Natural Selection*, 1958, p. 41 (abbr. *Sketch*).

14. *Ibid.*, p. 91 (abbr. *Essay*).

15. *Life and Letters of Charles Darwin*, 1887 (abbr. *L. & L.*), **2**, p. 116.

16. *Autobiography*, p. 118.

17. *Diary*, p. 103.

18. *Extracts from Letters Addressed to Professor Henslow*, by C. Darwin, privately printed 1835; repr. 1960, p. 7.

19. *J. of R.*, p. 209.
20. *J. of R.*, p. 108.
21. *Beagle*, p. 247.
22. *Darwin's Century*, 1959, p. 171.
23. *J. of R.*, p. 474.
24. *Beagle*, p. 246.
25. See note 10 *supra*.
26. *Journ.*, p. 7.
27. See note 11 *supra*.
28. Vol. 1, 1794, p. 487.
29. Notebook I, MS, p. 3.
30. Notebook II, MS, p. 4.
31. Notebook I, MS, p. 5.
32. *Ibid.*, p. 6.
33. *Ibid.*, p. 17.
34. 1821, vol. 5, p. 565. Quoted in Notebook I, MS, p. 142.
35. *Description physique des Iles Canaries*, 1836, p. 148.
36. Notebook I, MS, p. 158.
37. *Ibid.*, p. 8.
38. *Ibid.*, p. 14.
39. *Ibid.*, p. 54.
40. *Ibid.*, p. 10.
41. *Diary*, p. 435.
42. Lyell, 2, p. 90.
43. Notebook I, MS, p. 7.
44. *Beagle*, p. 263.
45. Notebook I, MS, p. 8.
46. Notebook III, MS, p. 175.
47. *Proc. Geol. Soc.* 2, 1837, p. 163; *Edinb. Phil. Mag.* 11, 1837, p. 542; cf. Eiseley, *Darwin's Century*, p. 163.
48. *Edinb. New. Phil. J.* 20, 1831, p. 394.
49. *J. of R.*, p. 209.
50. *J. of R.*, 2nd ed., p. 173.
51. *More Letters of Charles Darwin*, 1903 (abbr. *M.L.*), 1, 133.
52. Notebook I, MS, p. 113.
53. *Mag. Hist. Nat.* (N.S.), 1, 135, 1837.
54. *Proc. Amer. Phil. Soc.* 103, 94, 1959.
55. See notes 13 and 14 *supra*.
56. *Autobiography*, p. 119.
57. *Sketch for a Historical Picture of the Human Mind*, 1795.
58. *Enquiry Concerning Political Justice . . .* , 1796.

59. *Natural Theology*, 1802.
60. *Essay on the Principle of Population*, 1798 (Darwin seems to have used the 6th edition, 1826).
61. Notebook IV, MS, p. 136.
62. *A Reply to the Essay on Population*, 1807.
63. *Proposals for an Association*, 1812.
64. *Works, Letters and Journals*, 1898, 1, 332.
65. *L. & L.* 3, 237.
66. Notebook III, MS, p. 134.
67. Notebook III, MS, p. 65.
68. Notebook I, MS, p. 37.
69. Notebook III, MS, p. 175.
70. *Ibid.*, inside front cover.
71. *M.L.* 1, 118.
72. *Natural Theology*, 1802.
73. *The Temple of Nature*, 1802, Canto IV, lines 43 to 46.
74. *Philosophie zoologique*, 1, 99, 1809 (1873 repr., p. 112).
75. *Principles of Geology* (abbr. *Pr. of Geol.*) 2, 131, 1832.
76. *Dictionnaire des sciences naturelles*, 18, 384, 1820.
77. Notebook IV, MS, p. 114.
78. *Pr. of Geol.* 2, 175, 1832.
79. *Mag. Nat. Hist.* (N.S.) 1, p. 79, 1837.
80. *Proc. Amer. Phil. Soc.* 103, 101, 1959.
81. Notebook I, MS, pp. 115, 130.
82. Notebook II, MS, p. 177.
83. Notebook III, MS, p. 69.
84. *Notes & Records Roy. Soc.* 14, 52, 1959.
85. "An Account of a White Female Part of Whose Skin Resembles That of a Negro," in *Two Essays upon Double and Single Vision*, 1818.
86. *Naval Timber and Arboriculture*, 1831.
87. *Proc. Roy. Soc. Edinb.* 63, 361, 1950.
88. *Darwin's Century*, p. 202.
89. *Variation in Animals and Plants under Domestication* (abbr. *Variation*), 2, 431, 1868.

90. *Origin of Species* (World's Classics), p. 81.
91. *Edinb. New. Phil. J.* 4, 297, 1828.
92. Notebook I, MS, p. 118.
93. *Amaryllidaceae*, 1837, p. 347.
94. Notebook IV, MS, p. 111.
95. *Ibid.*, p. 137.
96. Notebook I, MS, pp. 46, 156, 157.
97. *De distributione geographica plantarum*, 1817, p. 39.
98. In *Pr. of Geol.* 3, 1833, Appendix.
99. *Phil. Mag. & J.* 68, 81, 1826.
100. *L. & L.* 2, 104.
101. *Ibid.* 2, 107.
102. *Ibid.* 2, 142.
103. *Trans. Ent. Soc. Lond.* 76, 367, 1928.
104. *Origin of Species*, p. 55.
105. *Sketch*, p. 42.
106. *Origin of Species*, p. 105.
107. *Ibid.*, p. 106.
108. *Ibid.*, p. 9.
109. *Autobiography*, p. 120.
110. *L. & L.* 3, 26.
111. *Origin of Species*, p. 112.
112. *Ibid.*, p. 113.

113. Notebook I, MS, p. 205.
114. Notebook IV, MS, p. 43.
115. *Ibid.*, p. 95.
116. *Ibid.*, p. 96.
117. Eiseley, *Darwin's Century*, p. 106.
118. *Life & Letters of T. H. Huxley*, 1900, 1, 170.
119. *The Genetical Theory of Natural Selection*, 1930.
120. *Essay*, p. 93.
121. *L. & L.* 3, 343.
122. *Variation*, 2, 92.
123. *Ibid.*
124. *M.L.* 1, 267.
125. J. Marchant, *Alfred Russel Wallace*, 1916, 1, 169.
126. *Variation*, 2, 70.
127. *Essay*, p. 100.
128. *Variation*, 2, 431.
129. *Autobiography*, p. 58.
130. Cf. R. A. Fisher, *Science Progress*, 27, 16, 1932.
131. I wish to express my thanks to Lady Barlow and Sir Alexander Carr-Saunders, K.B.E. for their kindness in reading the typescript of this lecture.

CHAPTER 5

pages 118–28

Ashley-Montagu, M. F. *Quart. Rev. Biol.* 10, 1935, 32, 181.
Augier, M. *C. R. Assoc. Anat.*, 1932, 18.
de Beer, G. *The Advancement of Science*, 42, 1954, 160.
———. *Embryology and Evolution.* Oxford, 1930.
———. *Embryos and Ancestors.* Oxford, 1962.
Bolk, L. *Das Problem der Menschwerdung.* Jena, 1926.
Broom, R. and C. W. H. Schepers. *The South African Fossil Ape-Men. The Australopithecinae.* Transvaal Museum Memoir, 2, Pretoria, 1946.
Buxton, L. H. D., and G. de Beer. *Nature*, London, 129, 1932, 940.

Le Gros Clark, W. E. *Early Forerunners of Man.* London, 1934.
Dart, R. A. *Nature*, London, 115, 1925, 195.
Devaux, E. *Trois Problemes: l'Espèce, l'Instinct, l'Homme.* Paris, 1933.
Dobzhansky, T. *Amer. J. Phys. Anthrop.* 2, 1944, 251.
Drennan, M. R. *Amer. J. Phys. Anthrop.* 16, 1931, 207.
Garrod, D. A. E., L. H. D. Buxton, G. Elliot Smith, and D. M. A. Bate. *J. Roy. Anthrop. Inst.* 58, 1928, 33.
Garstang, W. *J. Linn. Soc. London Zool.* 35, 1922, 81.
Giard, A. *Bull. Biol. France et Belgique*, 39, 1905, 153.

Gregory, W. K. *Amer. J. Phys. Anthrop.* 8, 1925, 373.

———. *Human Biology*, 2, 1930, 99.

———. *Man's Place Among the Anthropoids.* Oxford, 1934.

Hrdlička, A. *J. Roy. Anthrop. Inst.* 57, 1927, 249.

Huxley, J. S. *Problems of Relative Growth.* London, 1932.

Kalin, J. *Experientia, Basel,* 2, 1946, 272.

Keith, A. *Nature, London,* 153, 1944, 742.

Koenigswald, G. H. R. von. *De Ingenieur in Ned. Indie,* 1936, 149.

McKown, T. D. and A. Keith. *The Stone Age of Mount Carmel,* II. Oxford, 1939.

Martin, H. *Anthropologie, Paris.* 31, 1921, 331.

Morton, D. J. *Amer. J. Phys. Anthrop.* 7, 1924, 1.

———. *J. Bone and Joint Surgery,* 6, 1924, 56.

Sewertzoff, A. N. *Jena. Zeitschr. Naturwiss.* 63, 1927, 51.

Watson, D. M. S. *Proc. Zool. Soc.* London, 1918, 267.

Weidenreich, F. *Amer. J. Phys. Anthrop.* 3, 1945, 151.

Wood Jones, F. *Man's Place Among the Mammals.* London, 1929.

———. *Nature, London,* 159, 1947, 439.

Young, J. Z. "The Evolution of the Nervous System and the Relationship of Organism and Environment." *Evolution. Essays on Aspects of Evolutionary Biology Presented to E. S. Goodrich.* Oxford, 1938.

CHAPTER 6

pages 129–48

Broom, R. *The Mammal-like Reptiles of South Africa and the Origin of Mammals.* London, 1932.

Le Gros Clark, Sir W. E. *Man-Apes or Ape-Men?* New York, 1967.

Deevey, E. S. "The Human Population," *Scientific American,* 203, 1960, 195.

Edinger, T. "The Brain of Archaeopteryx," *Ann. Mag. Nat. Hist.,* Ser. 9, vol. xviii, 1926, 151.

Jarvik, E. On the Fish-like Tail in the Ichthyostegid Stegocephalians with Descriptions of a New Stegocephalian and a New Crossopterygian from the Upper Devonian of East Greenland. *Meddel. Grönland,* Bd. 114, No. 12, Copenhagen, 1952.

Oakley, K. P. "Swanscombe Man," *Proc. Geol. Soc. Lond.,* 63, 1952, 271.

Simpson, G. G. *The Major Features of Evolution.* New York, 1953.

———. "The Principles of Classification and a Classification of Mammals," *Bull. Amer. Mus. Nat. Hist.,* 85, New York, 1945.

Watson, D. M. S. "The Evolution and Origin of the Amphibia." *Philos. Trans. Roy. Soc.,* Ser. B. 214, 1925, 189.

———. On Seymouria, the Most Primitive Known Reptile. *Proc. Zool. Soc. Lond.,* 1919, 267.

White, E. "Australian Arthrodires." *Bull. Brit. Mus. (Nat. Hist.),* 1, 1952, 251.

Young, C.-C. "Mammal-like Reptiles from Lufeng, Yunan, China," *Proc. Zool. Soc. Lond.* 117, 1947, 537.

CHAPTER 10

pages 173–90

1. Gavin de Beer, *Atlas of Evolution* (London, 1964), map 9, p. 126.

2. H. F. Osborn, *Men of the Old Stone Age* (New York, 1921), p. 451.

3. André Varagnac, *L'homme avant l'écriture* (Paris, 1959), p. 361; "Le legs du mésolithique au néolithique," *Antiquités nationales et internationales*, fasc. III, 1960, Saint-Germain-en-Laye, p. 59.

4. Gavin de Beer, "The Volcanoes of Auvergne," *Annals of Science*, XVIII (1962 [1964]), 49.

5. P. Broca, "Instructions craniologiques," *Bull. Soc. Anthrop. Paris* (1875); G. Paul-Boncour, *Anthropologie anatomique. Crâne, Face, Tête sur le vivant* (Paris, 1912).

6. D. R. Brothwell, *Digging up Bones* (London, 1963), p. 89.

7. Gavin de Beer, *Embryos and Ancestors* (Oxford, 1962).

8. L. Manouvrier, "Sur les variations de la forme du crâne et de l'encéphale suivant l'âge et la taille," *Comptes Rendus de l'association pour l'avancement des sciences* (1882).

9. J. Ranke, "Die Schädel der altbayerischen Bevölkerung," *Revue d'Anthropologie* (Paris, 1882, 1884).

10. H. C. Jöhr, "Reduktionserscheinungen an den oberseitlichen Schneidezähnen (dominant gehäuft in einem Schwyzer Bergdorf)," *Archiv der Julius Klaus Stiftung für Vererbungsforschung, Sozialanthropologie, und Rassenhygiene*, IX (Zürich, 1934), 73.

11. G. P. Frets, "Heredity of Headform in Man," *Genetica*, III (1917), 193.

12. Gavin de Beer, *The Development of the Vertebrate Skull* (Oxford, 1937), p. 488; E. Augier, "Squelette céphalique," *Traité d'anatomie humaine* de A. Nicolas, P. Perrier et A. Charpy (Paris, 1931), pp. 83, 428.

13. C. S. Coon *et al.*, *Races* (Springfield, Ill., 1950).

14. J. F. Ewing, "Hyperbrachycephaly as Influenced by Cultural Conditioning," *Papers of the Peabody Museum*, XXIII (Harvard, 1950), no. 2.

15. Sonia Cole, *Races of Man* (London, 1963), p. 16.

16. C. S. Coon, "The Mountains of Giants," *Papers of the Peabody Museum*,

XXIII (Harvard, 1950), no. 3; B. Lundman, "Einige kritische Bemerkungen zur Anthropologie Vorderasiens," *Donum Natale H. S. Nyberg Oblatum* (1959), p. 87.

17. R. Ruggles Gates, "Race Crossing," *Genetica humana normalis*, II (Rome, 1962), 27; A. Schreiner, "Zur Erblichkeit der Kopf-form," *Genetica*, V (1924), 385.

18. A. E. Mourant, *The Distribution of the Human Blood Groups* (Oxford, 1954).

19. E. B. Ford, *Genetics for Medical Students* (London, 1956), p. 95.

20. C. D. Darlington, "The Genetic Component of Language," *Heredity*, I (1947), 269; A. E. Mourant and I. M. Watkin, "Blood Groups, Anthropology, and Language," *Heredity*, VI (1952), 13.

21. J. B. S. Haldane, *The Inequality of Man* (Harmondsworth, 1937), p. 73.

22. J. K. Moor-Jankowski, "La prépondérance du groupe sanguin O et facteur rhésus-négatif chez les Walser de Suisse," *Journal de génétique humaine*, III (1954), 25.

23. S. Rosin, "Die Verteilung der ABO-Blutgruppen in der Schweiz," *Archiv der Julius Klaus Stiftung für Vererbungsforschung usw.*, XXXI (1956), 17; J. R. Stoffel, *Das Hochtal Avers* (Zofingen, 1938).

24. J. B. S. Haldane, *op. cit.*, p. 71.

25. A. E. Mourant, *op. cit.*

26. Herodotus, II, 33; IV, 29; Festus Avienus, *Ora maritima*, 129.

27. Cato, *Orig.* fragm. 31.

28. Poseidonios, in Strabo, V, 2, 1; Roger Dion, "Géographie historique de la France," *Résumé des cours de 1958–1959*, *Annuaire du Collège de France*, p. 485.

29. Festus Avienus, *Ora maritima*, 130 ff.

30. W. H. Bullock Hall, *The Romans on the Riviera* (London, 1898), p. 47.

31. Scylax, 3 and 4; Raoul Busquet, *Histoire de Provence* (Monaco, 1956), p. 31.

32. Aristotle, *Meteorologica*, I, 13, 30.

33. Festus Avienus, *Ora maritima*, 674 ff.

34. Vittore Pisani, *Le lingue dell'Italia antica inoltre il Latino* (Torino, 1953), p. 267.

35. Giovanni Alessio, "Problemi di toponomastica ligure," *Convegno di studi apuani 1955, Rendiconti della terza giornata* (Carrara, 1956), p. 13.

36. Giuseppe Bottiglioni, "Per lo studio della vita popolare e delle parlate apuane," *ibid.* p. 5.

37. Information kindly supplied by Dr. A. D. H. Bivar.

38. Polybios, II, 16, 2; Pliny, *N. H.* III, 122.

39. *C.I.L.* V, 7749.

40. *C.I.L.* XI, 1147.

41. H. d'Arbois de Jubainville, *Les premiers habitants de l'Europe* (Paris, 1889, 1894), II, 46 ff.

42. Sallust, *Hist.* II; Solinus, T. Mommsen, *Collectanea* (Berolini, 1895).

43. Seneca, *De consolatione ad Helviam matrem*, 7, 8, and 9; R. M. Nicoli *et al.*, "L'origine des populations corses," *Etudes Corses*, no. 22 (1959), p. 11.

44. W. H. Bullock Hall, *op cit.*, p. 47.

45. Ptolemy, *Geogr.* III, 2, 8.

46. It is interesting that in the island of Alderney the word "clank" means exactly the same thing, as Mr. R. B. Freeman has kindly informed me.

47. V. Pisani, *op. cit.*, p. 278.

48. Emmanuel Anati, *La civilisation du Val Camonica* (Paris, 1960).

49. Clarence Bicknell, *The Prehistoric Rock-Engravings in the Italian Maritime Alps* (Bordighera, 1911); Nino Lamboglia, *Les gravures préhistoriques du Mont Bégo* (Bordighera, 1964). (Since the peace treaty of 1947 the frontier between France and Italy has been rectified and now includes Mont Bégo in France.)

50. Felix Staehelin, *Die Schweiz in römischer Zeit* (Basel, 1948), pp. 24, 167.

51. Ptolemy, III, 2, 5.

52. Caesar, *De bello Gallico*, VII, 90, 7; also *Anton. itin.; Peutinger Table; Not. dign. occid.* IX 32; *Geogr. Ravenna*, IV, 26, 238.

53. H. d'Arbois de Jubainville, *op. cit.*, II, 99 ff.

54. Jérome Carcopino, *Promenades historiques au pays de la Dame de Vix* (Paris, 1957), p. 9.

55. Fernand Benoit, *La Provence et le Comtat Venaissin* (Paris, 1949), p. 31.

56. Leibniz, letter to Abbé de la Charmoye 24 août 1701, quoted in Franck Bourdier, *Préhistoire et linguistique, les origines du Basque* (Paris, 1963–64), p. 2.

57. Élisée Reclus, *Nouvelle géographie universelle* (Paris, 1875).

58. F. Bourdier, *op. cit.*, p. 17.

59. Roger Dion, *Les frontières de la France* (Paris, 1947), p. 50.

60. E. C. Díaz, "El más reciente hallazgo de epigrafía ibérica," *Atti del 1º congresso internazionale di preistoria e protostoria mediterranea 1950* (Firenze, 1952), p. 179.

61. F. Ribezzo, "Sulla originaria unità linguistica e culturale dell'Europa mediterranea," *ibid.* p. 185.

62. Strabo, IV, 2, 1.

63. Strabo, III, 4, 17.

64. Diodorus, V, 14.

65. *C.I.L.* V, 7749.

66. Caesar, *De bello Gallico*, I, I, I.

67. Gabrielle Fabre, *Les civilisations protohistoriques de l'Aquitaine* (Paris, 1952).

68. A. E. Mourant, *op. cit.* The value for Berbers may need revision.

69. J. Moulinier, "The Rh. Factor in Southwestern Europe," *American Journal of Physical Anthropology*, VII (1949), 545.

70. P. B. Medawar, *The Uniqueness of the Individual* (New York, 1951), p. 123.

71. E. B. Ford, "Polymorphism and Taxonomy," *The New Systematics*, ed. Julian Huxley (Oxford, 1940), p. 493;

Ecological Genetics (London, 1964), p. 247.

72. Hugh O'N. Hencken, "Indo-European Languages and Archaeology," American Anthropologist, LVII (Menasha, Wis., 1955), memoir 84.

73. L. R. Palmer, Achaeans and Indo-Europeans (Oxford, 1955), p. 20.

74. Morris Swadesh, "Lexico-Statistic Dating," Proc. Amer. Phil. Soc. XCVI (1952), 452; "Archaeological and Linguistic Chronology of the Indo-European Groups," American Anthropologist, LV (1953), 349.

75. Tacitus, Agricola, II.

76. C. and J. Hawkes, Prehistoric Britain (Harmondsworth, 1952), p. 62; S. Piggott, British Prehistory (London, 1949), p. 83.

77. C. and J. Hawkes, op. cit., p. 72.

78. A. C. Thomas, Studies on the Folklore of Cornwall. 2. The Sacrifice (Camborne, 1952), p. 42.

79. G. Alessio, "L'origine du nom de Londres," Actes et Mémoires du IIIe congrès international de toponymie et d'anthroponymie, Bruxelles 1949 (Louvain, 1951), II, 223.

80. Ptolemy, II, 5, 7.

81. Ptolemy, II, 3, 12.

82. Lucan, VI, 67.

83. Bede's History of the English Church and People (Harmondsworth, 1955), p. 37.

84. Pliny, III, 48.

85. A. C. Thomas, Studies on the Folklore of Cornwall. 1. The Taboo (Camborne, 1951), p. 10.

86. G. Alessio, op. cit., II, 226.

87. The Problem of the Picts, ed. F. T. Wainwright (Edinburgh, 1955).

88. K. H. Jackson, "The Pictish Language," The Problem of the Picts, p. 129.

89. Bede's History, p. 39.

90. J. G. Frazer, The Golden Bough (London, 1922), p. 152.

91. Robert Graves, The White Goddess (London, 1961), pp. 50, 99.

92. K. H. Jackson, op. cit., p. 145.

93. C. and J. Hawkes, op. cit., p. 55; S. Piggott, op. cit., p. 74.

94. D. L. Gunn, P. M. Jenkin and A. L. Gunn, "Menstrual Periodicity," J. Obstet. Gynaec. British Empire, XLIV (1937), 839.

95. A. C. Thomas, The Sacrifice, p. 9; F. Benoit, op. cit., p. 261.

96. V. Gordon Childe, What Happened in History (Harmondsworth, 1960), p. 66.

97. C. and J. Hawkes, op. cit., pp. 60, 77.

98. Robert Graves, The Greek Myths (Harmondsworth, 1955); The White Goddess (London, 1961).

99. René Joffroy, Le trésor de Vix (Paris, 1962).

100. Tacitus, Ann. XIV, 36.

101. G. Lanson et P. Tuffrau, Histoire de la littérature française (Paris, 1912), p. 30.

102. Gavin de Beer, "Sur l'origine des Étrusques," Revue des Arts, V (Paris, 1955), 139; Route Annibal (Paris, 1962); "Iktin," Reflections of a Darwinian (London, 1962), p. 189; "The Malady of Edward Gibbon," Notes and Records of the Royal Society, VII (1949), 71.

Index